A pause outside the Roebuck for an Edward Martin photograph, here shown as a detail. The occasion is not recorded but was perhaps the Coronation of George V, as Arthur Haines was landlord at the Roebuck during the 1910s. This splendid turnout belongs to Arthur Cartlidge and his family.

Photographer – Edward Martin.
Source – Mrs Winifred Taylor.

a celebration of

the places and people of

MELBOURNE

DERBYSHIRE

in a portfolio of photographs

from the dawn of photography

and the eve of the new millennium

Today, the town's celebrations often end on the Junior School playing field with beer, skittles and balloons.

Photographer – Chris Brown.
Source – Melbourne Photographic Society.

FOREWORD

Melbourne is a small market town with over 4,000 residents on a fertile pocket of land which, in the past, was the main market gardening area for Derby. A thousand years ago it was a small Anglo-Saxon settlement close to Repton, the former capital of Mercia, and situated on a stream flowing into the River Trent a mile and a half to the north. It is 8 miles from Derby, just near enough, before the coming of the railways, for the local farmers to take their produce to Derby Market across the mediaeval Swarkestone Bridge and get home before nightfall. It had a fine Norman parish church, a Lancastrian castle and prosperous yeoman farms, and in the Middle Ages a new settlement was developed half a mile to the north at Kings Newton, within Melbourne Parish but still with a clear identity of its own.

By late Georgian times textile manufacturing had been added to Melbourne's farming and market gardening economy and it had become prosperous and non-conformist at the same time. But it never grew into a Derby or a Nottingham, its two giant neighbours, and for the past fifty years the town has been something of a sleepy backwater. The protection afforded to high quality farmland under post-war national planning policies restricted Melbourne's expansion, and this lack of development pressure has helped to preserve many fine Georgian and Victorian properties, often with new uses. Even the depredations of the local authority's clearance area programmes in the 1950s and 1960s were muted, though some attractive houses and industrial buildings were lost that could and should have been saved.

Towards the end of the nineteenth century Melbourne was a prosperous town with a growing middle class, and it was fortunate that a prolific and talented photographer, Edward Martin, was attracted to set up his studio in a house on Ashby Road in order to cater for the growing demand for photographic portraits and postcards of local village scenes. The majority of the black and white photographs in this book are his. We know very little about Edward Martin's background. He was born in Derby around 1852 and may have served an apprenticeship with one of the well-known Derby photographers such as Richard Keene or W. W. Winter, but by 1891 he was working in Melbourne from his studio in Ashby Road. He was a bachelor, and so far as we know had no family connections

in Melbourne. He stayed in Melbourne until 1920 when ill health forced him to retire and move to his sister's house in Derby where he committed suicide in April 1921.

In 1962, whilst 48 Ashby Road (not his studio home) was undergoing extensive repair, over 400 of Edward Martin's glass plates were discovered in the roof space. A number were broken and some had lost part of the emulsion, but many were in sufficiently good condition for them to be printed and privately circulated.

Melbourne Civic Society was founded in 1974, and a year later John Blunt, the owner of the plates, gave them to the Society. In 1988 a set of high quality prints was taken from most of the plates before they were deposited in the County Record Office at Matlock for proper conservation. These prints, together with some later additions to the archive, provide a unique record of Melbourne. Most of the surviving scenic views were taken around the turn of the century, and some of these have been printed in booklets published by the Civic Society and sold to raise funds for environmental improvements in the town.

To celebrate the new millennium, it was decided that Melbourne places and people should again be photographed and published alongside a selection of the historic prints so that future generations would have a similar record of Melbourne at the end of the twentieth century as the present generation has of the nineteenth, and be able to compare the two. This time, of course, we could use colour, the one element that is missing from all the early photographs.

Fortunately Melbourne has its own Photographic Society, and its members jumped at the opportunity of recording their town in this manner. The project was born as a partnership between the Melbourne's Civic and Photographic Societies, and has been supported by the National Lottery through the Heritage Lottery Fund and by South Derbyshire District Council.

This project has been carried out entirely by volunteers. Both societies are voluntary groups, and no-one has been paid to do the research or take the new photographs. Philip Heath, who has written the 'Short History of Melbourne' in this book and co-written, footnoted and edited the captions, lives in Melbourne and works locally, and we are immensely grateful for the efforts he has put in when he has so many commitments to the local community: he is a Committee Member of Melbourne Civic Society. The other member of our team has been Richard Heath (no relation), again a Civic Society Committee Member, who is himself no mean historian, who has helped with the selection and captioning of the historic photographs: he has also been invaluable, because of his local knowledge and contacts, in ferreting out previously unrecorded prints from the homes of old Melbourne families and persuading them to lend them to us for this publication. The new photographs are by members of the Photographic Society and each one is acknowledged by name.

The Project Team would like to thank the following for their assistance: John Blunt, Marjorie Calow, Eddie Cook, Gordon Foddy, Mary Fry, Lord Ralph Kerr, John Lord, John & Jean Parker, Harold and Mary Pipes, John Robinson, Howard and Lindsay Usher and Gill Weston.

We hope this book will be a treasured record of Melbourne's heritage, and help residents and visitors alike see and understand its buildings and people so that the best of the present can be preserved for future generations.

Ian Turner, Chairman of Melbourne Civic Society

Thomas Tivey, President of Melbourne Photographic Society

Members of Melbourne Photographic Society on location by Melbourne Pool: (left to right) Jenny and Robin Searle, Gavin Lake, Ken Leech, Peter Williamson and Thomas Tivey (President).

Photographer – Thomas Tivey.   Source – Melbourne Photographic Society.

The Millennium Project Team: From left to right; Philip Heath, Ian Turner, Thomas Tivey and Richard Heath.

Photographer – Thomas Tivey.   Source – Melbourne Photographic Society.

CONTENTS

Melbourne in 1640, *compiled from various sources*

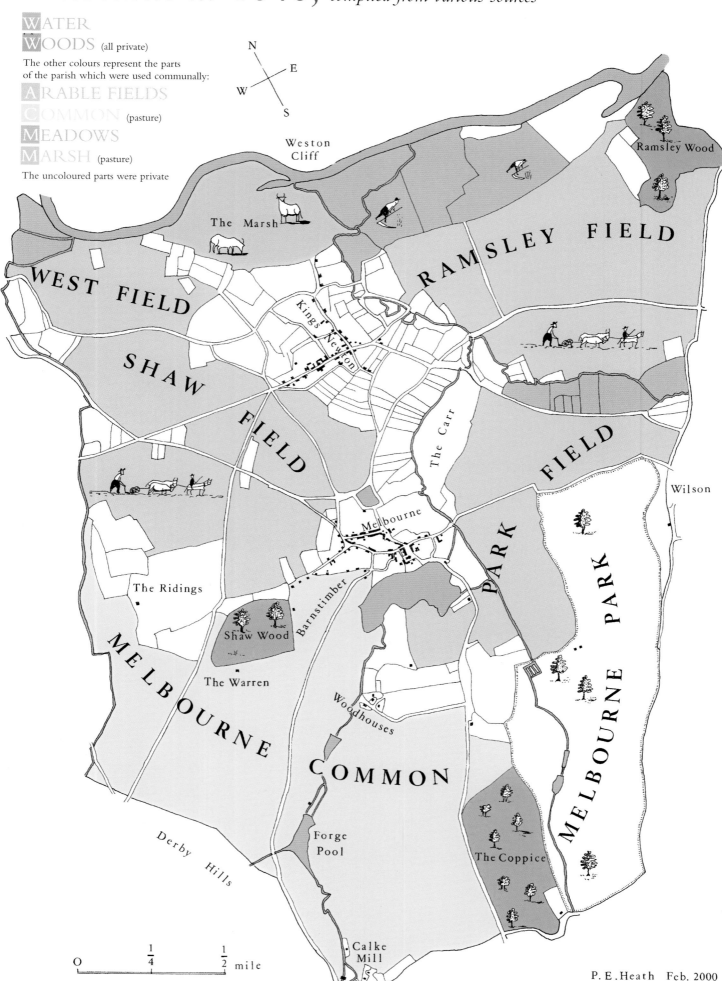

WATER

WOODS (all private)

The other colours represent the parts
of the parish which were used communally:

ARABLE FIELDS

COMMON (pasture)

MEADOWS

MARSH (pasture)

The uncoloured parts were private

N
E
W
S

Weston Cliff

The Marsh

Ramsley Wood

WEST FIELD

RAMSLEY FIELD

Kings Newton

SHAW FIELD

The Carr

PARK FIELD

Wilson

Melbourne

The Ridings

Barnstimber

Shaw Wood

The Warren

Woodhouses

MELBOURNE COMMON

MELBOURNE PARK

Derby Hills

Forge Pool

The Coppice

Calke Mill

O   ¼   ½ mile

P. E. Heath   Feb. 2000

A SHORT HISTORY OF MELBOURNE

AN AUSTRALIAN VISITOR TO MELBOURNE IN 1876.

In the Summer of 1876, an Australian visitor to England accidentally stumbled across a signpost to Melbourne. Knowing of no other Melbourne than the city in his own country, he made a detour to satisfy his curiosity. Arriving at the New Inn (now the Melbourne Hotel), he met the landlord Mr. Upton who:

> *"..had never heard of another Melbourne. My astonishment at such stupendous ignorance in no way flurried him ..... He called his wife to hear the wondrous news, and was to assemble the magnates of the town to meet me at tea-time"*[1].

The visitor boasted that his Australian Melbourne was very young, but had achieved far more in fifty years than the Derbyshire Melbourne had managed in 700. Some in the audience understandably took exception to this remark, because for a small place of little strategic importance, Melbourne was making rapid progress. Its growth and transformation from sleepy village to bustling little town were well advanced by the 1870s and continued until the First World War. At the time of the first national census in 1801 there were 1,861 inhabitants in the parish. By 1901 the number had almost doubled to 3,580.

It was modest growth compared to the meteoric rise of industrial towns such as Long Eaton, where the population rose from just over 900 in 1851 to more than 13,000 by 1901[2]. But the slower development of Melbourne was perhaps more healthy in some ways, enabling its old-established character and social composition to adapt gradually to new lifestyles instead of being swept aside by an overwhelming tide of change.

SOME NOTABLE PERSONALITIES

19th century Melbourne already attracted attention as an historic and attractive town. The Hall was a secondary seat of Lord Melbourne (1779-1848), who visited often during the 1840s when his term as Prime Minister had ended. He oversaw the remodelling of Melbourne Pool in 1843-6, which included the creation of the two islands[3]. His wife the notorious Lady Caroline Lamb (1785-1828) was once banished to Melbourne Hall, where her misdeeds were "no worse than walking through the muddy lanes in feathers and thin shoes and losing her temper with the local children"[4].

Lady Caroline Lamb who first coined the phrase

"Mad, Bad, and Dangerous to Know"

describing her lover, the poet Byron

Photographer - Thomas Tivey.

A similar view of Barehills today. The mill, now a private house, is visible between the two Lombardy Poplars. The trees in Lambert's Quarry have grown to overhang the public footpath which can be seen as a dark line on the pasture between two of Dennis Edwards' cows.

Photographer - Thomas Tivey.

Source - Melbourne Photographic Society.

A view from Ashby Road looking towards Melbourne Pool. The building in three separate parts facing the camera is the mill. To its right, seen here between the two islands, is the miller's house now known as Pool Cottage. In the foreground is the "Barehills", probably so called because the surface of the ground had been 'bared' to test its suitability for quarrying. Lambert's Quarry, one of Melbourne's largest old gritstone quarries, lies beyond the wall on the left. The wood in the middle distance on the right is known as Brickkiln Pits or the Elders, and conceals the dank pools from which clay was extracted for bricks in the 18th and 19th centuries.

Photographer - Edward Martin.

Source - Melbourne Civic Society.

Lord Palmerston, another of Queen Victoria's Prime Ministers, was also acquainted with Melbourne, having married Lord Melbourne's sister Emily in 1839. He laid the foundation stone of the Athenaeum on Potter Street in 1853, noting that its combined functions as an Infants' School, Mechanics' Institute and Savings Bank catered for the needs of man from youth to old age[5].

Melbourne was also the birthplace of Thomas Cook (1808-1892) who, in 1874, made an unsuccessful bid for the tenancy of Melbourne Hall[6]. Having been born in poor circumstances and made his own fortune, he was perhaps trying to make a point. His professed aim to bring hordes of tourists to Melbourne, until a "grand hotel" was needed to accommodate them, provoked alarm and was probably one reason why his application was declined. Cook left his mark on Melbourne by building a group of Memorial Cottages in 1891 (see page 63).

Melbourne's first historian John Joseph Briggs of Kings Newton (1819-1876) must also be given credit for raising an awareness of the area's history and charm, both locally and nationally. In his *History of Melbourne* (1852) he notes that Melbourne had attained a position of considerable importance in the County during the previous century, and that "a spirit of industry and thrift" was indicated by the constant improvements which were taking place.

THE LANDOWNING STRUCTURE
OF THE PARISH

Melbourne's proud, progressive and independent spirit was able to develop in the absence of domination by a single landowner. The Burdetts of Foremark and the Harpur Crewes of Calke had unchallenged authority in neighbouring villages such as Ticknall, Calke, Stanton by Bridge, Swarkestone and Milton. Large landed estates were not generally promoters of urban industry. Investment in agriculture was a more certain way of increasing the income from rents than industrial investment, which could be speculative or risky and might also attract poor immigrants who could become a burden on the parish.

At Melbourne the landowning situation was rather more favourable for industrial development. There were two major estates in the parish at the dawn of the 19th century: the Melbourne Estate increased and became more dominant as the century progressed; the Donington Estate, on the other hand, faded into relative insignificance. Neither estate enjoyed a monopoly over the affairs of the parish, and there was a large number of small freeholders free to invest in their properties as they saw fit. In 1808, just under half of the parish's 3,464 acres belonged to Lord Melbourne's Estate, which comprised 1,686 acres. The Donington Estate in Melbourne at that time comprised 924 acres. Through piecemeal purchase and exchange, Sir Henry Harpur 7th Baronet of Calke had added 138

acres of Melbourne parish to Calke Park during the late 1780s. The remaining 716 acres of the parish in 1808 were divided among lesser estates, that of the Cantrells of Kings Newton being chief among them[7]. The Donington Estate sales of 1811 and 1813 released more land to these lesser landowners, thus allowing Melbourne to open itself even more freely to industrial enterprise.

However, the power of the two principal estates should not be under-estimated. Both were important forces in the development of Melbourne, and it is appropriate at this point to give a short résumé of their histories.

THE MELBOURNE ESTATE

The Melbourne Estate was originally a Rectorial estate, given by King Henry I out of his Royal Manor of Melbourne to Adelulf, first Bishop of Carlisle. Henry I founded the Bishopric of Carlisle in 1133, possibly to reinforce his control of Cumbria which had been conquered by his brother William II in 1092. His reason for giving the new Bishop an estate at Melbourne may have been to ensure his continued loyalty to the English Crown, countering the potential influence of Henry's brother-in-law, David I of Scotland[8]. In addition to the Rectory estate, Adelulf was also given a life grant of the King's Royal Manor of Melbourne; the same privilege was granted to Bishop Walter Malclerc, one of Bishop Adelulf's successors, in the 1220s.

M page 8

Except on part of the north side, the Parish Church is tightly hemmed in by houses and old farm buildings. This unusual view of the west end shows a glimpse of the great west door viewed through a gap which was formerly the gateway into a farmyard. The building on the right is the Tithe Barn, which was converted to a malthouse by John Earp around 1800[1]; it has lain vacant for many years. The slated roofs of the western towers of the church, added during the Victorian restoration, were criticised by some connoisseurs of church architecture, but they made the building distinctive and not everyone was pleased by their removal in 1955.

Photographer - Unknown.

Source - Melbourne Civic Society (Dashwood Fane Album).

It is certainly an exceptional building and is recognised as one of the finest Norman parish churches in England.

The distinctive original form of Melbourne Parish Church, with a western gallery and a two-storeyed chancel, suggests that it was of a high status and built either by the King or the Bishop. Stylistically it is thought slightly to predate the foundation of the Bishopric, so it is perhaps more likely to have been built by King Henry I as part of his Royal Manor of Melbourne. It is certainly an exceptional building and is recognised as one of the finest Norman parish churches in England.

It was probably during the 12th century that a new settlement or "new ton" (ton = farm) was laid out in the King's manor of Melbourne, called Kings Newton to distinguish it from other Newtons such as Newton Solney. It may have been grafted onto the western side of an earlier settlement, but further research is required into this idea. Bishop Walter Malclerc obtained the grant of a weekly market at Kings Newton in 1231, having obtained the grant of a market and annual fair for Melbourne in the previous year. The steps of the mediaeval market cross at Kings Newton still remain, now surmounted by a modern cross to commemorate the accession of King Edward VIII.

There has long been a cult of separatism between Melbourne and Kings Newton, and the gulf between them widened as their economies went separate ways. While Melbourne became (to Newton eyes) a vulgar manufacturing town, Kings Newton retained quiet dignity as a time-honoured farming village, scarcely touched by the 19th century. There is a fine assortment of old houses along the Main Street, praised by the late Sir Nikolaus Pevsner as "one of the most attractive village streets in Derbyshire"[9] (see pages 58-9).

As time passed, the Bishops of Carlisle visited Melbourne less frequently and by the early 16th century their Melbourne estate was rented out under lease, including the Rectory house which is now Melbourne Hall. In 1592, the Rectory was leased to Sir Francis Nedham[10], who partially rebuilt the dilapidated old house[11] and also built up his own freehold estate at Melbourne. At the heart of it was the former Royal hunting park of Melbourne, which he purchased in 1598[12]. The park was probably enclosed around 1200 by King John, who visited the manor house at Melbourne several times; parts of the ditch and bank around the park still survive. In 1629 Sir Francis Nedham sold his estate to Sir John Coke, who took a new lease of Melbourne Hall from the Bishop in the same year. Sir John's descendant Lord Ralph Kerr still lives in the Hall with his family today.

Melbourne Hall has been in the hands of the same family since 1629, although the family name has changed three times due to inheritance through the female line. The current residents are the Kerr family, seen here in the gardens. Ralph Kerr is holding Hugh, and Marie-Claire is holding Minna. Between them is Jamie, with Amabel, Francis and Johnnie in front. Molly (the dog) is on the left.

Photographer - Thomas Tivey.

Source - Melbourne Photographic Society.

The Cokes gradually enlarged and consolidated their estate through purchases and careful management. In 1734, for example, George Lewis Coke bought the Derbyshire estate of the Hardinge family of Kings Newton[13], including Kings Newton Hall. The freehold of Melbourne Hall was acquired from the Bishop in 1704, giving the Rt. Hon. Thomas Coke the security he needed before laying out the famous formal gardens. They include notable lead statuary from the Hyde Park Corner workshop of Jan Van Ost, and an outstanding piece of virtuoso wrought ironwork called the "Birdcage" made by local smith Robert Bakewell in 1706-8. The Hall itself was remodelled into its present form soon afterwards. The west wing was rebuilt by Francis Smith of Warwick, architect and builder, in 1726-7 and the east wing was rebuilt by his son William Smith of Warwick in 1744-5. Older work remains visible on the north side. The house and grounds were let to tenants for most of the 19th century, so are less altered than they might otherwise have been.

Vast sums of money were spent on the improvement of the estate during the 19th century. The farmland was re-arranged and farmsteads rebuilt, and the surroundings of the Hall and Pool were greatly enhanced. The family returned to the house permanently in 1905, but a large portion of the estate was sold off shortly afterwards, in 1919. Most of the estate now lies within the south-eastern quarter of the parish, still having the former Royal Park as its nucleus.

The "Birdcage" made by local smith Robert Bakewell 1706-8, and the man who commissioned the work; the Rt. Hon Thomas Coke (1674-1727), painted by Michael Dahl.

Source - Derbyshire Countryside Ltd

A drawing of Melbourne Castle made for Queen Elizabeth I around 1576 (Public Record Office). The Castle was built between 1311 and 1322 - a "magnificent building" - but only ever half finished.

THE DONINGTON ESTATE

In about 1605, the former Royal Manor of Melbourne was sold for £4,700 to Henry, 5th Earl of Huntingdon, who had a seat at Donington Hall (now the headquarters of British Midland Airways). Although the parish of Melbourne is contiguous with Donington Park, the Earl and his successors never showed much interest in the further development of their Melbourne estate. On the contrary, a third of it was sold at auction in 1811 and 1813 due to reckless overspending on Donington Hall and Park. Further sales were made in 1866, and the estate virtually disappeared with the sale of Castle Cottage, Castle Farm and the adjacent farmland in 1914.

When the 5th Earl bought the Manor, it included Melbourne Pool and its watermill, which serve as a reminder that Melbourne got its name from two Old English words: "myln" = mill and "burna" = stream, hence "millstream" - a stream easily dammed and powerful enough for turning mills. The mill and pool passed to the Melbourne Estate through an exchange agreement in 1789[14].

The 5th Earl's purchase also included Melbourne Castle, built by Thomas Earl of Lancaster and his steward Robert Holand between 1311 and 1322, no doubt on the site of the previous manor house.

It was a "magnificent piece of building", but was only ever half finished owing to the unsuccessful rebellion of the Earl of Lancaster against King Edward II. The Earl of Lancaster was executed, and Robert Holand was murdered a few years later[15].

In 1583, it was proposed that Mary Queen of Scots should be sent to Melbourne Castle and a survey was made to assess its suitability. It stated that the rooms were "great and spatious" but few in number, that the ground around was marshy and unpleasant, and that the house (being unfinished) was "left imperfect at every corner"[16]. So the proposal was abandoned, and when the Earl of Huntingdon bought the Manor of Melbourne the destruction of the redundant castle began in earnest. It had virtually gone by about 1630. Substantial foundations were uncovered at various places on the site during the 19th century, and an area excavated in 1967 remains exposed on private land. Even in their fragmentary state, the foundations still demonstrate the startling quality of the building.

After the destruction of the castle a new manor house was built on its site[17], from which the Donington estate home farm in Melbourne was run. The manor house was eventually subdivided and incorporated into the factory of Thomas Haimes and Co. until its final destruction by fire in 1933 (see pages 42 and 54).

MELBOURNE MILLS

Relationships between the Melbourne Estate and Donington Estate were sometimes frosty, as illustrated by a dispute over watermills during the 1630s. Melbourne Pool and the Mill were then part of the Donington Estate of the 5th Earl of Huntingdon. Sometime before 1621, Sir Francis Nedham of Melbourne Hall built a new mill on his own land adjacent to the Earl's old mill[18]. In doing so he created a potential problem, because the Earl owned and controlled the water supply to it from Melbourne Pool.

Sir Francis Nedham sold his mill to Sir John Coke along with the rest of his estate in 1629. The potential water problem became real in about 1632, when the Earl of Huntingdon severed the supply. The precise reasons behind his action are not known, but during the 17th century there were recurring disputes over the trade due to the mills, and the water supply available from Melbourne Pool was said to be inadequate for the Earl's mills, let alone anyone else's. Around the same time, the Earl replaced his own mill with the building which now survives (see page 36) and was accused of adding insult to injury by encroaching on Sir John's land in the process.

Sir John was thus left with a watermill that had no water, and which stood useless until he rebuilt it in 1636 on a new site, almost a mile and a half away on his Derby Hills estate. The mill probably stood there for less than seventy years, but the stone-faced mill dam still survives under the Staunton Harold Reservoir, and has been exposed in drought conditions[19].

It is not known when the brook was first dammed to form a head of water for Melbourne Mill. Tradition says that stone for Melbourne Castle was quarried here before the area was flooded, but there is no firm evidence. In the right background is an area of old 'ridge and furrow' ploughland, preserved under grass after the Melbourne Estate bought it to improve the view from the Hall in the 18th century. On the horizon, the front of the farmhouse at Park Farm (the Melbourne Estate Home farm) can be seen among the trees. The farm was built between 1834 and 1840[2] to replace earlier buildings flanking Church Close. It stands within the old Royal Hunting Park, probably enclosed by King John around 1200.

Photographer - Edward Martin.   Source - Melbourne Civic Society.

Sir John Coke (1563-1644) by Cornelius Jannsens
Source - Derbyshire Countryside Ltd.

The present view of the Pool from the Church tower is little changed, but the disappearance of many parkland trees on the horizon has opened up a fine view of Breedon Church and a not so welcome line of electricity pylons.

Photographer - Thomas Tivey.   Source - Melbourne Photographic Society.

THE ENCLOSURE OF
THE OPEN FIELDS

It was in the mutual interests of the Donington and Melbourne Estates to lay aside any past grievances and collaborate over the Parliamentary Enclosure of Melbourne in 1787-91, which was an important precursor to the development of 19th century Melbourne. "Enclosure" was the term used to describe two broad processes.

One purpose was the re-organisation of the age-old "open field" system, whereby all or most farmers of a village had scattered, narrow strips of arable land unfenced from each other in large fields. The fields were cropped in rotation, and the crops had to be sown and harvested communally. At Melbourne there were in effect three open fields consisting of Shaw Field to the west, Ramsley Field to the east and two smaller fields called Park and West Field which were separate from each other but cultivated as though they were

one. Meadow and pasture land were similarly apportioned. With the onset of the Industrial Revolution and rapid increase of population, it was desirable that farmers should be able to experiment and progress by diversifying their crops. The initiative for enclosure came mainly from landowners and substantial farmers, who had capital available for investment. They wanted large, well laid out farms where all the land was in one convenient block, and where they could be free of the outmoded restrictions attached to the old open field system.

THE COMMON

The other purpose of enclosure was to bring land into cultivation which had previously been uncultivated. In the case of Melbourne, this land comprised Melbourne Common, formerly a Crown woodland of some 740 acres, which was part of the manor of Melbourne bought by the Donington estate. Melbourne Wood was cleared at some time in the forty years before 1623[20], and was afterwards known as the "Common" or "Waste" instead.

The term "waste" implies that the Common was of little use, but this is a misconception. Many parishioners possessed "common rights", allowing the owners or tenants of old established houses to use the common in a variety of beneficial ways. Sheep and horses were put there to graze, and pigs to forage for beech-mast and acorns. The common also provided brushwood for ovens, furze and gorse for fires, and stone for building.

THE COPPICE, THE WARREN AND THE FURNACE

The successive Earls of Huntingdon, as owners of the land, also made the Common work for themselves. On the east side 75 acres were enclosed by them as a "coppy" or "coppice". The coppice was divided into quarters and the trees were cut down in rotation while the growth was still young to provide a continual supply of thin poles. New growth was continuously produced by the old stools, which could remain productive for centuries.

On the south side of Robinsons Hill the Earl had an extensive rabbit warren, which was let to tenants and run as a business. Rabbits were a valuable source of food, but by the 18th century there was mounting concern in Melbourne about the damage done by them both to the usefulness of the Common and to the neighbouring farm land. Complaints to the Earl of Huntingdon were unheeded, and in 1750 the warren was attacked and virtually destroyed. The warren recovered from the onslaught, but within a few decades it was abolished during the Enclosure[21]. In the middle of the Common the Earl had an iron forge on the stream, replaced in the early 18th century by a blast furnace which was let to Birmingham Ironmasters until 1772. The remains of the furnace were excavated by W. H. Bailey in 1958, prior to the flooding of the site by the Staunton Harold Reservoir.

After the enclosure of the Melbourne open fields in 1787-91, the promotion of market gardening was led by Samuel Robinson who "converted a waste into a smiling garden." [3] At its peak in the 1930s eighty eight family units provided the local markets with fresh fruit and vegetables. The photograph shows the firm of Hatton Brothers and Snape in typical gardeners' uniform.

Photographer – Unknown.
Source – Mrs Winifred Taylor.

STONE QUARRYING
AND BRICK MAKING

The Common was also a source of good building stone and brick clay. In 1761, the Earl of Huntingdon leased the gritstone quarries on Melbourne Common to John Chambers, stonecutter, of Wilne[22]. Chambers came to live in Melbourne, and the house he built at No. 15 Potter Street around 1789 still survives. After his death, his widow Mary and then his son William continued in business at Melbourne until 1848.

An undated view of No. 15 Potter Street from an upper window of the Athenaeum. The house was built by Melbourne stonemason John Chambers around 1789, but the tenancy was taken over in 1849 by John Pass, a wheelwright[4]. This intriguing picture shows the wheelwright's yard on the right, later to become part of Nixon Knowles' timberyard which closed for redevelopment in 1994. The attractive curved wing walls at each end of the house no longer exist.

Photographer - Unknown.   Source - Richard Heath.

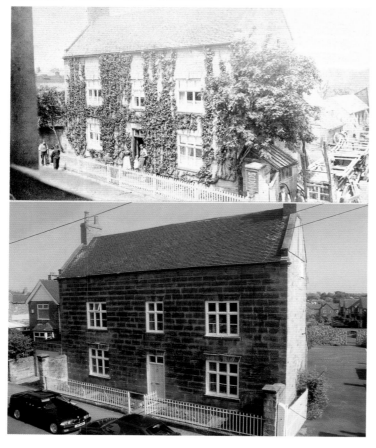

15 Potter Street is now known as "Exchange House", so-called because from the late 1920s until 1966 it was the town's manual telephone exchange: it is now a private house. The yard to the right is now part of J. P. Springthorpe & Co., funeral directors. The rest of the former woodyard has been redeveloped for housing as an extension of Jubilee Close, originally laid out in the Jubilee year of 1977. The woodyard site was marketed by its developers (Bryant Homes) as "Mulberry Knoll", a source of combined indignation and amusement among the local population.

Photographer - Robin and Jenny Searle.   Source - Melbourne Photographic Society.

Their chief business was the manufacture of special stones for sharpening scythes, but they also supplied building stone. Throughout this period, it was common practice to build the fronts of Melbourne houses in brick, using rough stonework for the gable ends and the backs. Where required, the Chambers would supply good quality dressed stonework too, which can still be seen in many buildings around the area. Items were transported further afield from a warehouse of stone and thatch by the River Trent[23]. The quay can still be seen on the site today.

From the early 18th century to the mid 19th, Melbourne's most prominent family of brickmakers were the Warrens. Henry Warren of Derby made bricks for Melbourne Hall gardens in 1704 and was presumably the same Henry Warren that rented a brick kiln on Melbourne Common from the Earl from 1707 onwards[24].

The business premises of both the Chambers and the Warrens were on the edge of the Common at Woodhouses, conveniently sited for easy access to both the clay pits and stone quarries. A primitive range of 18th century sheds, once used for making scythe stones, can still be seen there.

THE ENCLOSURE PROCESS

In those places where all the relevant land belonged to one person, he could order an enclosure himself. Parliamentary Enclosure Acts, obtained in a similar way to other Acts of Parliament, became common after 1750 and were necessary in cases where opinions about enclosure were divided. By obtaining such an Act, an enclosure could proceed despite opposition provided that the owners of most of the land affected were in favour of it. In these circumstances, those in opposition were forced to submit to enclosure of their land.

The Melbourne Enclosure Act, which provided the power to enclose, was obtained in 1787. The land and interests of all property owners within the area were then to be evaluated so that land of equal value could be allotted to them in the re-structured layout. Where appropriate, the road system would be re-arranged for greater convenience. Equally important was the need to compensate the commoners for their common rights, and this was done by awarding them their own plots of land on the western side of the common along the Ticknall road. This is in fact the only part of the former Melbourne Common that is still called "The Common" today. The rest of the Common was divided among a few large farms belonging to the Melbourne estate and thereby lost its identity.

▲ *Woodhouses was originally a small settlement on the edge of the 740 acre Melbourne Wood. Some of the properties there can be traced back to the 16th century, but the hamlet found a new purpose in the 18th century when the stone and clay deposits on the Common began to be exploited on a large scale for building. Since the later 19th century, when the local brickmaking and stonemasonry industries began to wane, Woodhouses has shrunk a little and lost some of its buildings.*

Photographer – Edward Martin.
Source – Philip Heath

▼ *In recent years, some former gardening ground in the Robinsons Hill / Calke Road area has been converted to pasture by the owners of adjacent houses in order to improve the views from their homes and to enhance their settings. As a result, sheep graze land that was once intensively cultivated. However, market garden crops can still be seen in the background of this view of Woodhouses.*

Photographer – Thomas Tivey.
Source – Melbourne Photographic Society.

The Enclosure Award, i.e. the deed by which the Common and open fields were officially divided, was finally signed and sealed in 1791. The reaction of the parishioners in general to its contents is not well documented. The influential tenants of the Melbourne and Donington estates no doubt thought it prudent to keep any negative views to themselves. However, in Thomas Dugmore, owner and landlord of the former Bull's Head Inn on Potter Street (now nos. 50-54), Melbourne had one remarkable personality who refused to be silenced. Dugmore was so incensed by the proceedings of the Enclosure Commissioners (the professional agents that designed the Enclosure) that he was moved to publish a pamphlet in 1800 called *Observations on Inclosing the Manor of Melbourne*, in which he aired his grievances at length.

Thomas Dugmore was:

"a somewhat remarkable and eccentric character,.........most methodical and exact in all his dealings with his customers. If a party went into his house and called for a gallon of ale he would draw the quantity in separate pints to shew that full measure was given. If one of his household put on the teakettle to boil and was absent when it boiled he allowed it to boil over and waste to the last drop before he would take it off conceiving as he observed 'that he had no right to interfere with the business of another'. A person met him one morning and accosted him 'Good morning Mr. Dugmore - a fine morning'. 'Fool' said he 'don't you think I know it'[25]" !

Dugmore's coldly logical mind was equal to the niceties of the Melbourne Enclosure Award, which would have intimidated most of his contemporaries - had they dared to challenge it. In his pamphlet he criticises technical errors and inconsistencies in the Award, as well as the unjustness of some of its provisions.

THE ALTERATION OF THE MAIN ROAD

One of Dugmore's chief complaints concerned the re-routing of the main road from Derby through Melbourne towards Ashby-de-la-Zouch. Until 1789, this road departed from its current route at the west end of Queensway, and proceeded to the north end of Castle Street via what is now Beech Avenue and the grounds of the Grange. The road then followed Castle Street to the parish church, and Pool Road to the weir. From the weir, it headed for Melbourne Common Farm, and on to Coppice Farm, rejoining the present route at the Leicestershire boundary.

During the Enclosure, a new road was laid out to replace the old one. To use modern reference points, it followed existing lanes from the west end of Queensway to the Thomas Cook Memorial

Cottages on High Street. Beyond this point, High Street originally petered out into a track towards St. Bride's Farm, and part of this track is preserved in the path from Washington Close to the recreation ground on Cockshut Lane. From the Thomas Cook Memorial Cottages through Woodhouses and to the Leicestershire boundary the new road was entirely new.

Dugmore pointed out that the old road was gently graded, direct and more practical than any other which could possibly be substituted. The new road traversed the valley at Woodhouses, which is steep on its southern side and was much steeper before the cuttings and embankment were made in 1855[26]. The reason for the diversion, as everyone always knew, was to give greater privacy to Melbourne Hall. In today's more leisured society, everyone is able to enjoy the aesthetic benefits that the removal of the road brought to the environs of the Hall and Pool, but in an 18th century context the validity of Dugmore's argument is hard to deny.

MELBOURNE'S FIRST NEW STREETS

The re-routing of the main road had a profound effect on the growth pattern of Melbourne. Until 1789, Castle Square was the centre of the village. It is still identifiable as such, being the largest open space in the street layout and close to the Parish Church, the old graveyard, the former Town Well (in front of No. 65 Church Street), the remains of the Castle, and Melbourne's oldest pub the "White Swan" rebuilt in 1682.

Even before the Enclosure, the west end of Melbourne was the fastest growth area because land was available for development, and new streets had already been laid out there. The first, laid out in 1777[27], was simply called the New Yard. The next two were called after the fields they were built on, namely Blanch Croft (laid out in 1783)[28] and Quick Close (laid out in 1797-8)[29].

No one had the foresight to make any of these new streets more than twelve feet wide, making them an obvious target for clearance projects of the 1960s. Clearance work was well advanced on New Yard before there was a change of heart. It was re-named Thomas Cook Close, as if in penance for the demolition of his birthplace on Quick Close, which was completely redeveloped. Blanch Croft, once destined along with New Yard for clearance as the route of a town centre bypass, fortunately remained relatively unscathed. Many of the houses on New Yard, Blanch Croft and Quick Close were built for owner-occupiers. They differed, therefore, from the next new streets of Melbourne, which consisted mostly of speculative housing of a lower class, built on land sold by the Donington estate in 1813. Called Selina Street, Rawdon Street, Hastings Street and Moira Street, they were collectively known as

"New York" or "The City". The housing was cheap and crowded and the inhabitants gained a reputation for rough and unruly behaviour. In a house on Rawdon Street, a butcher brutally murdered his wife in April 1885, exclaiming afterwards that "she was a bad 'un" and that he "ought to have done it sooner". The case was minutely reported, complete with the grisly details, in the 'Derby Daily Telegraph'. Since the Second World War, the New York area has been completely redeveloped.

An austere view of Castle Square (the original market place) from the south end, taken before 1890. This picture well illustrates the haphazard arrangement of the buildings, which seems to have been the result of gradual encroachment onto the Square. Of all the main streets in Melbourne, this location has suffered more than any other from wanton and accidental destruction. The two houses in the foreground were demolished following bomb damage in 1940, and the block of houses beyond was condemned to demolition in 1963 as part of the local authority's clearance programme[5].

Photographer – Unknown.   Source – Richard Heath.

RE-ESTABLISHMENT OF THE MARKET

In 1836, a weekly market was re-established at Melbourne, held on Saturdays for the sale of butter, poultry, vegetables etc. Castle Square was no longer at the main junction of roads in Melbourne, and therefore no longer the natural rendezvous, so the market made its home on the present Market Place instead. During the 19th century, many of the Market Place frontages were either re-developed or built up for the first time, often incorporating shops (see pages 54-55). Castle Square on the other hand was left to stagnate, and prospective building land in that vicinity failed to attract investment. The buildings around Castle Square are generally older than those in the Market Place because there was little motive for redeveloping property there. Melbourne has thus been left with two market places, very different in character.

MIGRATION OF THE FARMS

Before the Enclosure, when most of the farms had land scattered across the parish, it was logical for the farmsteads to be sited within the village. But after the Enclosure, village farmsteads were slowly abandoned in favour of sites amid the newly consolidated blocks of land. Despite long disuse, some fossilised farmsteads still survive in the middle of Melbourne, where they continue to have an enormous impact on the street scene:

Carter's (or Brown's) Yard on High Street was a farmstead until the death of John Carter in 1823, when it was purchased and developed for houses and cottage industries by the Melbourne Hall estate. The kitchen wing of the former farmhouse, thatched and with a distinctive pair of cruck blades at its western gable, remains a landmark in Melbourne today. Some of the houses which flank the yard at the back of the house are converted from former farm buildings.

▶

In 1976, after 150 years of being subdivided, the Cruck Cottage was restored by its new owners Barry and Patricia Cheshire and reunited as a single house. The old smoke-blackened thatch of local straw, several feet deep in places, was completely stripped and replaced by local thatcher David Raffles at the end of his three-year apprenticeship with George Mellor of Cromford. Today, thatching practices have changed and wholesale removal of old thatch is avoided wherever possible.

Photographer - Thomas Tivey.

Source - Melbourne Photographic Society.

▲

This view of High Street is dominated by the gable end of the Cruck Cottage, which has recently been tree-ring dated to 1530[6]. The Cruck Cottage was formerly a farmstead on the Kings Newton Hall estate, and was sold to John Carter in 1727. The Carters stayed there until 1823, when William Carter died without an heir. The Melbourne Estate bought the property and set about converting the old farmhouse and outbuildings into cottages and workshops. The thatched part of the farmhouse was originally the kitchen wing[7].

Photographer - Edward Martin.

Source - Melbourne Civic Society.

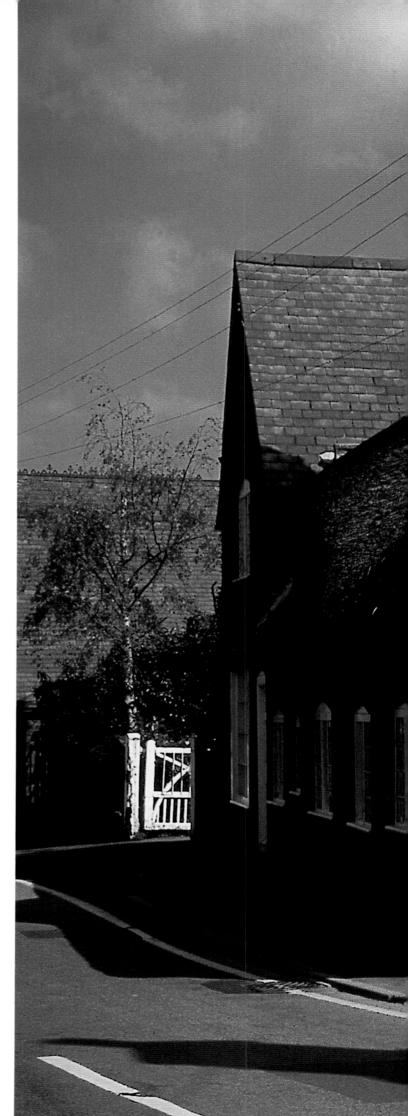

The **Dower House** farmyard has been divided up since 1813, when the former open footpath across the middle of the farmyard was walled in to form the present "Dark Entry" leading from the Parish Church to Penn Lane (see pages 67 and 71). However, if an effort is made to "think away" the entry walls, it can be seen that the farmbuildings all around the yard still remain intact. The Dower House was built in 1821, and replaced a most interesting old house occupied in the 16th century by the Bewley family, bailiffs of the Manor of Melbourne.

Melbourne Hall's farm buildings were adjacent to the house, supplemented by another yard of farm buildings on the west side of Church Close. These were the home farm buildings of the Melbourne Hall estate until 1840, when a new farmhouse and outbuildings were completed in the old Royal Park (see page 11). Again, the old buildings near the Hall remain remarkably intact 160 years after losing their original function, including an important mediaeval aisled barn.

FRAMEWORK KNITTING AND THE SILK FACTORIES

James Pilkington, writing in 1789[30], noted that a considerable number of the Melbourne inhabitants were already engaged in manufacturing industries:

"Many hands are employed in combing and spinning jersey. But those who work upon the stocking frame are still more numerous, there being no less than eighty of these machines within the parish. The stone quarries near the town also afford employment to about thirty persons. The chief part of their business is the manufacture of scythe stones."

This page: A selection of silk gloves and mittens, for which Melbourne was renowned. These were made by Thomas Haimes and Co. and probably date from the period c.1840-1880. (Photographed by Thomas Tivey by courtesy of Peter Newbury)

Photographer - Thomas Tivey.

Source - Melbourne Photographic Society.

Framework knitting as a cottage industry appears to have become widespread in Melbourne during the last quarter of the 18th century. Workers in this industry were probably the main cause of population growth in Melbourne, and the parish registers record a very noticeable spate of framework knitters' marriages in the 1780s. At this period Melbourne specialised in worsted (i.e. woollen) hosiery.

The usual framework knitting machine of this period was about three feet wide, and the knitters worked the frames in their own homes. A high proportion of new housing in late Georgian Melbourne was built by or for framework knitters, especially in newly developed areas of the village along High Street, Derby Road, "The Puzzle" (now redeveloped) at the north end of Castle Street, and the new streets at New Yard and Blanch Croft. The knitting shops can be distinguished by their large amount of glazing, often in long windows with high sill levels designed to throw maximum light onto the frames at the appropriate height. The knitting shops were usually integral with the houses, as at nos. 7, 11, 19 and 45-57 Blanch Croft, and nos. 81-85 Castle Street.

During the period from about 1820-1840 Melbourne switched from the production of woollen hosiery to the production of lace, especially silk lace, made on larger frames which were inconvenient to have in the home. Some framework knitters were already working in buildings which were structurally independent of their houses, but the shift to silk lace making made the practice more common and heralded the move towards full-scale factory based production. Small detached or semi-detached workshops remain at the backs of no. 35 Derby Road, no. 28 Ashby Road, the rear of 28a Market Place and the rear of 52 Derby Road.

William Haimes, founder of Melbourne's best known and longest lived hosiery firm, had come to Melbourne from Leicestershire by 1785[31] as a woolcomber, worsted maker and hosier. His elder son William carried on in his father's footsteps, but the younger son Thomas applied his inventive mind to copying the figured silk items produced by France. In 1812, after much experimentation, he succeeded. His most famous product was a beautiful silk shawl, which remained popular until a change in fashion during the 1830s. Silk gloves then became the main product. By 1840, the Haimes's main factory was Castle Mills in Castle Square behind the former Manor House[32]. It was extended in 1850, and in 1853 Melbourne's first steam engine was built there[33].

Of the other textile manufacturers in Melbourne, the most important were the Hemsleys. They had been framework knitters in the late 18th century, and quickly rose to prominence as silk glove manufacturers during the mid 19th century. Thomas Hemsley, whose premises were at "The Puzzle", was so successful that he was able to buy the large Highfields Farm at Melbourne for £10,000 in 1845, instantly making him the fourth largest landowner in the parish after Lord Melbourne, the Marquis of Hastings and Sir John Harpur Crewe[34]. His two sons each built substantial new factories. William Hemsley built Kendrick Mill on Chapel Street and his brother John built the huge Victoria Mill on Derby Road, where Budgens supermarket now stands. The ceremonial laying of the foundation stone of Victoria Mill in February 1861 was a pretentious affair, accompanied by a procession and music, and was the source of some local amusement and ridicule[35].

BOOT AND SHOE MAKING

Kendrick Mill and Castle Mills continued producing silk goods into the 20th century, but in the 1860s John Hemsley's Victoria Mill was turned over to the mass production of boots and shoes. Perhaps he foresaw that the free trade agreement with France in 1860 would make silk manufacture less profitable. Shoemaking had been carried on as a cottage industry for centuries, but during the 1860s and 1870s large and expensive new machines had been introduced for

pressing out soles and joining them to uppers. These machines were unsuitable for the home, and by the 1890s all shoemaking processes had finally been brought into factories. John Hemsley died in 1880 and his pioneering Victoria Mill was dramatically destroyed by fire ten years later, while owned by the Messrs. Parker. (see page 44). It was less than thirty years old, but its short life had already shown that Melbourne's future now lay in boots and shoes rather than silk.

Collyer Bros.' boot and shoe factory on Derby Road, later Dunnicliff Bros., taken around 1900. Once typical of Melbourne, it is a rare survival although now used as the 'Picture of Health' fitness studio.

Photographer - Edward Martin.
Source – Melbourne Civic Society.

The success of Victoria Mill spawned a whole generation of smart red brick boot and shoe factories in Melbourne, but unfortunately they are poorly represented today. The best remaining example is the former factory of Collyer Bros. on Derby Road, taken over by Dunnicliff Bros. in 1905 and now a health and fitness club. Other notable examples included the Wellington Boot Factory on Church Street (demolished), the West End Boot Factory on South Street (built in 1882 and burnt down in 1947), the Mount Boot Factory of Loake Bros. on Commerce Street (built in 1894 and rebuilt after a fire in 1939), and the Victoria Boot and Shoe Factory of John Coxon on Victoria Street (burnt down in 1896 when only about five years old)[36]. Coxons had been long established as a family of cottage shoemakers in Melbourne, and the factory had been built with fifty years' savings. The boot factory of John Wilson & Co. on Derby Road (now Doncasters plc) should also be mentioned, but is not strictly in the same category as it was originally built by Joseph Bullock, a builder, joiner and timber merchant (see page 44).

MARKET GARDENING

This brief account of Melbourne industry is incomplete without the inclusion of industries dependent on the land. One of these was the cultivation of osier beds for basket making. Most of them were on the Donington estate in the north east corner of the parish adjoining Donington Park, but there were small areas elsewhere in the parish. They appear to have been let to basket makers outside the parish (e.g. at Castle Donington), so in practice the industry did not have much direct bearing on Melbourne. Market gardening, by contrast, came to be synonymous with Melbourne.

The pioneer of market gardening in Melbourne was Samuel Robinson of Shaw House on Robinsons Hill, which was named after his family. His fame as a gardener came from his success in cultivating the unpromising land on the edge of the former Melbourne Common during the early 19th century, but his interest in the subject had evidently been instilled by his forebears, who were already growing large quantities of hawthorn plants or "quicksetts"[37]. One of the fields used by the Robinsons for this purpose came to be known as Quick Close, which name it has kept despite long being built over.

The popularity of quicksetts at this time can be explained by the Enclosure movement, and the industry later gained a new lease of life through the need to fence railways. One of Melbourne's leading nurserymen, John Buck, built a new house opposite the bottom of Cockshut Lane around 1860 and christened it "Hawthorn House". Later houses along Derby Road followed suit with other botanical names, including The Poplars (now Conery House), The Limes, The Laurels and The Hollies. Samuel Robinson's farm at the Shaw was large, but he was a conventional gentleman farmer as well as a market gardener. When the enthusiasm for market gardening caught hold among the working class during the 1850s, it was not found necessary to have an extensive holding in order to make a living.

The Robinsons' farm was rented from the Melbourne Estate and Samuel Robinson was evicted after a bitter lawsuit in 1873, despite much moral support from the local community. He was succeeded at Shaw House by James Salsbury, another prosperous gardener and another self-made man. Salsbury was the driving force behind the laying out of Victoria Street in 1887 and the building of the Liberal Club on Derby Road in 1889 (see page 61). He took a particular interest in fruit growing, and at his death in 1898 he had shares valued at £1250 in the Midland Fruit Preserving Company at Chesterfield[38]. In 1903, an experimental "fruit plot" was set out on Salsbury Lane, inspired by lectures given by a horticultural instructor from Derbyshire County Council.

Today, Bill Sharp and his family still make a living from a traditional market garden on the Newton Lane/Derby Road corner. Here, they are using a modern planting machine to plant out lettuce seedlings.

Photographer - Thomas Tivey.

Source - Melbourne Photographic Society.

With the development of the global economy, the importance of Melbourne's market gardening industry is much reduced. Of about ninety family gardening businesses before the Second World War, only a handful survives. The legacy of market gardening is not obvious in the street scene, but profits from the industry were responsible for some of the individual houses and terraces on Melbourne's new Victorian streets. In the fields beyond and around, the stripey market garden landscape survives only in isolated pockets. Isolated brick buildings and a few neglected lines of orchard trees are the most evocative reminders of its former importance.

MELBOURNE: TOWN OR VILLAGE ?

Most Melbourne residents like to think of it as a village, because it seems the most appropriate word to describe its modest size, facilities and community spirit. But despite all the cosy connotations of a village, it is an insult to the enterprising spirit of 19th century Melbourne to call it anything other than a town.

The transformation from village to town was noted by visitors. In 1789, Melbourne was described as a large and well-looking village[39], and was still described only as a "considerable village" in 1821. By 1846, following the re-opening of the market, it was at last described as an "improving market town" and by 1857 as a "small, pleasant and well-built market town"[40]. The 19th century was an exciting and optimistic time, when development and growth instilled a sense of pride rather than alarm. Feelings often ran high, with a lot of plain speaking and protracted public slanging matches in the local newspapers[41]. Today, with the decline of Melbourne's industrial economy, it might be argued that Melbourne has changed from a town back to a large village.

It was during the 19th century that Melbourne became a self-conscious place, aware of how it looked and of what impression it made on the world outside. Its public buildings were deliberately designed to make an impact and serve as ornaments. In short, Melbourne developed a town mentality.

Improvements gathered momentum in the 1850s. The building of the Athenaeum in 1853 has already been noted (see page 6) and in 1859-60 the Parish Church was restored under the direction of Sir George Gilbert Scott. This marked the end of its rustic interior with whitewashed walls, box pews and coat pegs fixed to the pillars. The restoration was accompanied by a new cemetery with spiky gothic cemetery chapels on Packhorse Road, designed by Benjamin Wilson and opened in 1860. The Parish Church had long ceased to be the religious hub of the parish, and the new cemetery had separate areas for members of the established church and Nonconformists.

The Nonconformist churches were thriving, with the exception of the Quakers, whose chapel probably closed in the 1830s. The Baptists enlarged their existing chapel, while the other denominations built impressive new premises of arresting design, using rock-faced stone. The Swedenborgians built their new chapel on Derby Road in 1863-4, designed by Benjamin Wilson[42]. The Methodists followed with a substantial new chapel on Church Street in 1869-70 (see pages 26-27), designed by Messrs. Wilson and Willcox of London and Bath[43]; the old chapel next to it was converted to a schoolroom shortly afterwards. The Independents (now the United Reformed Church) built a new chapel and schoolroom on High Street in 1871-2, designed by G.H.Sheffield. They replaced older rented premises of 1779 on Penn Lane, which were converted to a house (now Huntingdon House) in 1874[44].

The provision of educational facilities was a source of much friction between the Church of England and the Nonconformist churches. The Council of Education criticised a lack of school facilities in the parish in 1873, but the handsome Board School on High Street was not built until 1897, after years of wrangling[45]. It was designed by Henry Beck of Burton on Trent (see page 62).

Services improved as well. In 1853 a gasworks was built, and the opening was celebrated by lighting a large star of 650 gas burners in the top end of Potter Street[46]. The railway between Derby and Ashby was opened in 1868, with a station for Melbourne at King's Newton (see pages 48-50). In 1877 a public sewerage scheme was introduced[47], and attention soon turned to the provision of a better water supply. Eventually, Melbourne and Castle Donington joined in a scheme to supply Long Eaton with water from boreholes and a pumping station on the edge of the parish, adjoining Stanton by Bridge, which opened in 1892. By 1900 Melbourne was smart and self-assured. Many of its buildings were fairly new, its footpaths were neatly paved with brick and kerbed with stone, and amply lit with gas.

Opposite: This view of the interior of the Parish Church is the earliest in the book, taken prior to the restoration of 1859-60. The irregular box pews, crude heating stove, limewashed walls and coat pegs fixed to the pillars produce a homespun character. Most people today would prefer the unrestored state to the sober Victorian re-arrangement, which perhaps says more about propriety than people.

Photographer - Unknown.
Source - Melbourne Civic Society (Dashwood Fane Album).

Opposite: This view of the Church interior, probably taken around 1900, shows the results of the restoration. The joints and detailing of the stonework appear more crisp, owing to the removal of the limewash. The three decker pulpit has gone, and the Dawson monument on one of the northern pillars has been removed out of sight to the south aisle. The chancel screen, removed in 1937, was mediaeval but altered and heavily restored in 1859-60 and 1891[8]. Its absence from the early photograph is hard to explain. Perhaps it had already been dismantled for restoration.

Photographer - Edward Martin.   Source - Melbourne Civic Society.

The quiet approach to Melbourne from the east is known as Blackwell Lane after the former mansion of the Blackwall family, swept away for an extension to the Hall gardens in the 17th century. The cottage seen in the background of this view was altered and given a tiled roof in 1890[9], and the other cottage had the same treatment in 1903[10]. Nevertheless, the view remains instantly recognisable today.

Photographer - Unknown.
Source - Melbourne Civic Society
(Dashwood Fane Album).

Melbourne Market Place

A particularly attractive view of Melbourne Market Place (formerly the Greenhill) looking east, before 1885[11]. A century earlier, the thatched cottages in the centre would have been unchallenged in scale, but by the late 19th century taller buildings had become the norm. These cottages have survived, but the roofs have been raised and slated. The three storey building on the left was demolished to make way for the new Co-op building of 1915. The buildings on the right hand side are still with us, but the Methodist Church of 1869 has unfortunately lost its impressive spire.

Photographer - Unknown.

Source - Richard Heath (Warren Album).

PHOTOGRAPHY

Photography arrived in Melbourne too late to capture
the early stages of its transformation, but some remarkably
early photographs remain.

Some were taken by Richard Keene, possibly including those of the
Parish Church taken in 1858 prior to its restoration. James Earp of
High Street also took some early photographs of Melbourne in the
1860s, including stereoscopic views[48]. Edward Martin was born
around 1852 and had set up his business in Melbourne by 1891[49]. He
continued it for thirty years until, in 1920, health problems and
constant pain caused Martin to sell his business. His place at the
forefront of Melbourne photographers was taken by W. Mayell, but it
is not currently known whether Mayell actually bought Martin's
business. Meanwhile, Martin had gone to live in Derby where, in April
1921, he hanged himself [50].

It was a sad and poignant end for someone who spent his life recording
celebrations and happy events. But the era he captured so well had
already ended. With the First World War, the rapid development of
Melbourne slowed down dramatically. Ambitious new buildings
ceased to be built and the population stagnated. Whether he realised it
or not, Edward Martin had captured Melbourne during one of the
most exciting periods of its history.

Philip Heath, Melbourne, September 1999.

*A modern wintery photograph of the same scene which was reproduced as a popular
Christmas card. The granite cross bears silent witness to the Parish's
losses in twentieth century conflicts.*

Photographer – Robert Brunt.

MELBOURNE'S SETTING AND APPROACHES

The parish of Melbourne occupies a shallow valley containing the brook from which Melbourne takes its name. The brook is bordered by fertile land on an outcrop of gritstone, and is a tributary of the River Trent which forms the northern boundary of the parish. The town itself stands on the western slope of the valley.

This archetypal chocolate-box photograph of 1888 has a dreamlike quality, and shows a cruck framed labourer's cottage on Trent Lane, Kings Newton. Originally an independent small farmstead, it was later annexed to Elms Farm[13]. It was picturesque but clearly in need of repair, and the Melbourne Estate decided to replace it. This photograph, from the Melbourne Hall archives, was probably specially commissioned as a souvenir prior to demolition. Trent Lane once gave access to a ferry over the River Trent, long discontinued.

Photographer – Unknown.

Source – Melbourne Hall Muniments.

Here is the same view a year later showing the replacement house, now known as "Crown Cottage" after the motif on the date plaque. The flood plain of the River Trent is just visible in the background. The house, now extended and painted white, looks like the work of the Melbourne Estate consultant architects Evans and Jolley of Nottingham.

Photographer – Unknown.

Source – Melbourne Hall Muniments.

The eastern approach from Wilson along Blackwell Lane, with the high stone wall of Melbourne Hall gardens on the left and cottages on the right.

Photographer - Thomas Tivey.

Source Melbourne Photographic Society.

The southern approach from Staunton Harold on the Ashby Road. The first property in Melbourne proper is the eighteenth century Melbourne Arms on the corner of Robinsons Hill, which now incorporates an Indian restaurant. The daffodils were planted by the Civic Society in November 1998, and are a spring feature of many of Melbourne's approach roads.

Photographer - Thomas Tivey.

Source Melbourne Photographic Society.

The Hollow, off Penn Lane, about 1887. Here were the animal pens on the edge of the common, which probably gave Penn Lane its name. As time passed, humble cottages were built in the pens, some of them having mud walls[14]. The oldest cottage that survives is the one in the centre foreground, now much altered. After the pool was remodelled in the 1840s the area became fashionable, and some of Melbourne's most prestigious houses can now be found there.

Photographer – Edward Martin.   Source – Richard Heath, Warren Album.

This autumn view, close to the viewpoint of the previous photograph, shows how the modern houses have been 'absorbed' into the landscape by extensive garden tree planting: indeed, the Pool is barely visible. The horse chestnut trees on the right in Brown's Field provide a crop of conkers for local children - and their dads.

Photographer – Thomas Tivey.   Source – Melbourne Photographic Society.

The bridge over Blackwell Brook (as this section of the brook is called) was a favourite playground, having a ford alongside it as shown in the photograph. The bridge lay on the route to the horse fair at Belton, and the locals returning from the fair would throw pennies into the brook, to be retrieved by the local children with a lot of rough-and-tumble[15].

Photographer – Edward Martin.   Source – Melbourne Civic Society.

THE MILLS

There were several mills and mill pools along the course of the brook. Melbourne Mill, complete with its attractively landscaped mill pool, was probably always the most important and is the only one to survive.

The Windmill was built by the first Lord Melbourne in 1797-98[16] to help supplement the old water mill by Melbourne Pool. It was advertised 'to let' in 1846, described in the Derby Mercury "...as having three pairs of stones in good working order with good trade and having five acres of grassland let with it.[17]" It was disused by 1882[18], and shows considerable dereliction in Martin's photograph.

Photographer – Edward Martin.

Source – Melbourne Civic Society.

In 1963 the remains of the Windmill were gutted and converted by the River Dove Water Board into an observation tower with a fine view of the new Staunton Harold Reservoir, but it was never opened to the public[19]

Photographer – Thomas Tivey.
Source – Melbourne Photographic Society.

The mill may occupy the site of Melbourne's Domesday mill, but there is no proof. The present building was constructed by the Earl of Huntingdon in the 1630s using stone from Melbourne Castle[20], and was raised and refitted in 1832-3 to the designs of William Frost of Nottingham (millwright) and Thomas Cooper of Derby (architect)[21]. It closed in 1968[22] and was converted to a house in 1973[23]. Only the top floor of the main mill building can be seen in this view; the two lower storeys are built against the dam.

Photographer – Thomas Tivey.

Source – Melbourne Photographic Society.

One of Edward Martin's classic studies of Melbourne Pool. The print was fastened to glass, given a green velvet surround with gold trim, and offered for sale to the general public. It shows the twin pyramidal spires of the church, added during Sir Gilbert Scott's restoration of 1859-62 and known locally as the "pepperpots". They were removed in 1955[24].

Photographer – Edward Martin.

Source – Richard Heath.

This 1999 view across the Pool is taken from the footpath in King's Field, much further back than Martin's classic photograph. (The island from which Martin's photograph was taken is on the left). This is probably the least changed and most loved view of Melbourne.

Photographer – Thomas Tivey.

Source - Melbourne Photographic Society.

▲ *An idyllic view of Furnace Farm looking westwards across the valley towards the windmill, whose sails can be seen behind the trees on the horizon. The substantial stone farmhouse and outbuildings were demolished around 1960 to make way for the Staunton Harold Reservoir, which now covers the site. The farm took its name from a water powered 18th century blast furnace for smelting iron ore, built by Messrs. Mander and Weaman of Birmingham (Ironmasters) on the site of an earlier forge, probably in 1726[25]. It was taken over by Sampson Lloyd of Birmingham in 1758[26] and ceased operation in 1772[27]. In 1789 the furnace was demolished[28] and the furnace house became a farmhouse. Substantial remains of the stone-built furnace came to light during excavation in 1957-60, including a section of the waterwheel[29].*

Photographer - Edward Martin.

Source - Melbourne Civic Society.

▼ *Furnace Farm would have been under the sailing boat in the centre of this picture, which is taken from the public car park near the windmill. Water Utility Companies used to keep the public well away from their drinking water reservoirs and catchment areas, but this photograph shows a new approach which is people (especially family) friendly, with outdoor recreation facilities, extensive landscaping and areas set aside for wildlife conservation.*

Photographer - Thomas Tivey.

Source - Melbourne Photographic Society.

THE RURAL ECONOMY

Melbourne's land has been cultivated for both arable and dairy farms, but most famously for vegetables and fruit. Its minerals, particularly the gritstone and clay deposits, supported thriving rural industries in the 18th and 19th centuries.

A refreshingly informal view of about 1887 showing a farmyard at Woodhouses, home to Thomas "Wangups" Jackson, his wife and their eleven children. Thomas Jackson is probably the figure in the right foreground. The farmhouse and most of the outbuildings had been rebuilt by the Melbourne Estate in 1884 after the previous tenant, Charles Gregory, had "fallen into evil ways" and practically deserted the farm[30]..

Photographer - Unknown.   Source - Philip Heath.

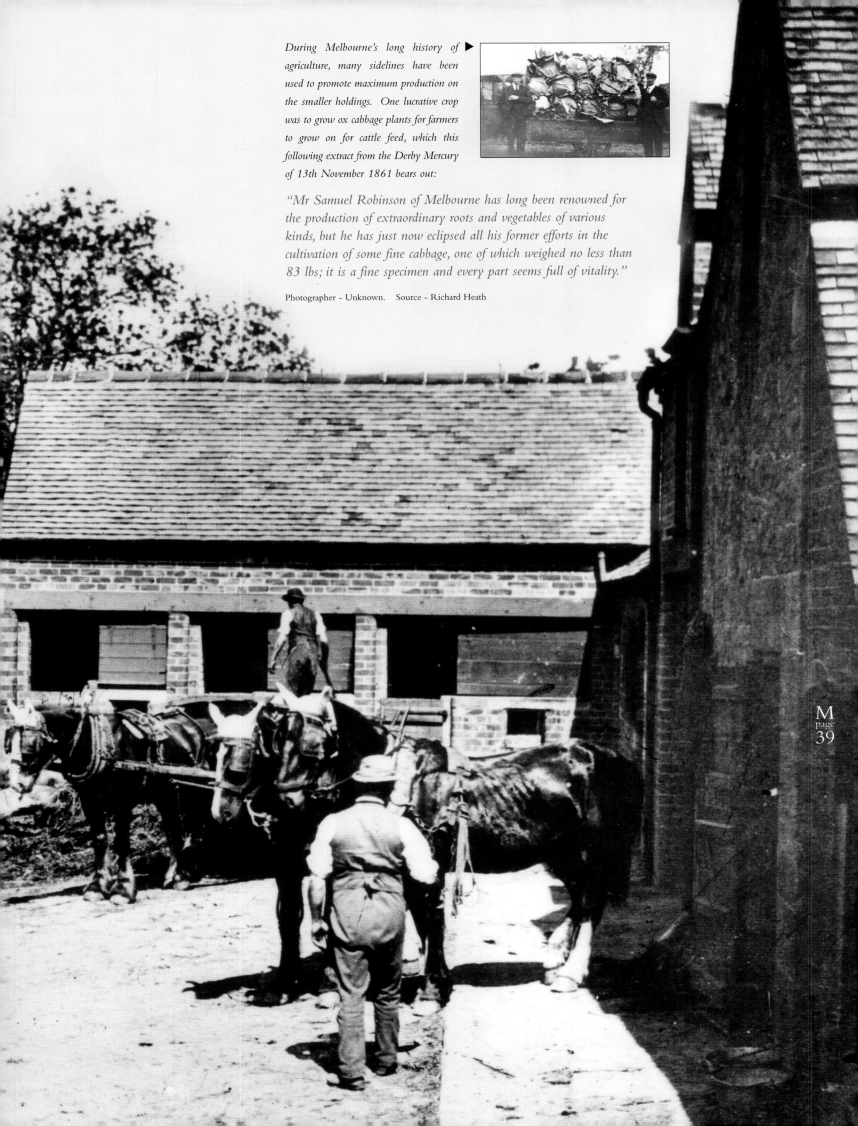

During Melbourne's long history of ▶ agriculture, many sidelines have been used to promote maximum production on the smaller holdings. One lucrative crop was to grow ox cabbage plants for farmers to grow on for cattle feed, which this following extract from the Derby Mercury of 13th November 1861 bears out:

"Mr Samuel Robinson of Melbourne has long been renowned for the production of extraordinary roots and vegetables of various kinds, but he has just now eclipsed all his former efforts in the cultivation of some fine cabbage, one of which weighed no less than 83 lbs; it is a fine specimen and every part seems full of vitality."

Photographer – Unknown.   Source – Richard Heath

Since the 1970s there has been a major decline in the Melbourne market garden industry, and several of the survivors, such as Messrs. F. M. Heath and Son here at Woodhouse Farm Nurseries, now combine vegetable and flower growing, a garden centre and farm shop. This photograph of primroses in a polytunnel was taken on Mothering Sunday, 1999.

Photographer – Thomas Tivey.

Source – Melbourne Photographic Society.

A view from the Hilly Field Allotment Gardens, developed by a newly formed "Melbourne Allotment Holders' Association" in 1920, with 53 plots of 600 square yards each. They were sold on lease for £16-10-0d per plot, and strict rules governed the management of the plots. In all, over 36 acres were laid out in various parts of the parish, mainly on low rents for "cottagers" to subsidise their income growing fruit and vegetables, starting with "Lord Melbourne's Potatoe (sic) Land" in 1843 [31]. The Hilly Field Gardens are still well cultivated, and the plotholders enjoy a fine view over the town.

Photographer – Thomas Tivey.

Source – Melbourne Photographic Society.

Most of Melbourne's farmland is now used for grain crops, and this is a typical late summer scene - a combine harvester at work at Derby Hills Farm.

Photographer - Thomas Tivey.

Source - Melbourne Photographic Society.

A view looking north over Melbourne from the top of the church tower, around 1893. In the centre is the large factory chimney of Thomas Haimes and Co.'s Castle Mills, with the former Manor House to its left and the factory to the right. The gasworks of 1853, with a chimney of its own, can be seen to the right of the factory. With the aid of a magnifying glass it is possible to read the description "mountain railway" on one of the funfair wagons assembled in Castle Square.

Photographer – Edward Martin.

Source – Melbourne Civic Society.

OTHER INDUSTRIES

Melbourne, like most towns, was once self-contained with the usual wide range of shops, public houses and service industries. The handsome independent factories for textiles, boots and shoes contributed to the distinctive character of the place. Today, in line with the general trend, its economic independence has gone.

This modern view, taken during Wakes Week, shows many changes. Castle Mills was demolished in 1989, having closed a few years earlier, and was replaced in the 1990s by a bland housing development. The gas works closed after the nation-wide introduction of natural gas. The large three storey house in the foreground, known as The Lodge, was destroyed by one of a string of bombs dropped over Melbourne in 1940, and its site is now the car park to the Senior Citizens' Centre. Hulse's shop on the Castle Street corner has been incorporated back into the house, now known as the "Pump House", although the former water pump, clearly visible in the previous photograph, has also disappeared. In the background are the extensive pre- and post-war housing estates on Melbourne's northern edge.

Photographer – Thomas Tivey.

Source – Melbourne Photographic Society.

"Edward Thompson, Woollen Draper and Tailor, Hatter, Hosier, Outfitter etc - every Requisite for all Degrees of Freemasonry." Occupying, in turn, two of the most prominent positions in the Market Place, this epitome of Victorian elegance was established in 1845[32], finally closing as a family business in the 1950s.

Photographer – Edward Martin.

Source – Melbourne Civic Society.

Thompson's shop at 38 Market Place is now Wayne Spiers, Melbourne's only surviving butcher. The fascia and outer frame are all that remain of the elegant Victorian shopfront.

Photographer – Peter Clough

Source – Melbourne Photographic Society.

Victorian factory chimneys like this were once a common sight in Melbourne. This substantial example built by Joseph Bullock as part of his joinery works, probably in 1869[33], is the sole survivor today. In the 1920s, a Melbourne man recalled the nervous excitement of watching Melbourne bricklayer Tom Mear take down the timber scaffolding, balancing like a tightrope walker from pole to pole along the top edges of the planks with nothing to hang on to, scores of feet in the air.[34]. After Joseph Bullock's death in 1898, the works were taken over by John Wilson, boot manufacturer, who lived at No. 65 Derby Road[35].

In 1990, the single storey buildings in front of the original building were removed. The building was sensitively altered and repaired for office use by John Blunt (pictured) of Castle Farm and his son Richard, with Melbourne architect Adrian Earp. Particular pride was taken in the retention and repair of the redundant factory chimney, and the site was re-named "Wilson's Yard" to maintain the historic link.

Photographer – Thomas Tivey.   Source – Melbourne Photographic Society.

Victoria Mill in Derby Road was built in 1861 as a textile mill by the Hemsley family, but at the time of the fire on November 24th 1890 it was used to manufacture boots and shoes.

Photographer – Edward Martin.   Source – Melbourne Civic Society.

For over 100 years the Dallman family, with its bakehouse round the corner in Potter Street, provided a valuable service to the local community, subsequently carried on at the premises by Bartrams, Hughes and finally Burnetts. This was the last of the Melbourne bakeries to close.

Photographer – Edward Martin.   Source – Richard Heath.

Panties have now replaced pastries, but the 'Promises' lingerie shop is still recognisable from 100 years ago. The timber fascia, blind and pilasters are original, as is the glazed brick stallriser. The cast iron cresting above the shopfront is the main loss.

Photographer – Thomas Tivey.   Source – Melbourne Photographic Society.

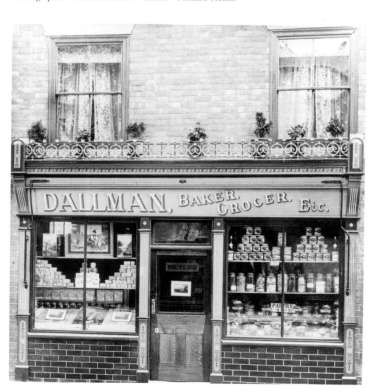

After the fire at Victoria Mill the site was progressively developed. Part of it became the garage and workshops of Parker and Bradley, eventually to become the "Melbourne Engineering Company" and another part housed the Trent Bus Garage until 1994, when it closed. In 1996, the arrival of Budgens, a supermarket chain based in the south of England, contributed to the closure of several traditional food shops in Melbourne, but it also attracted Melbourne custom back from out-of-town stores.

Photographer – Thomas Tivey.

Source – Melbourne Photographic Society.

The Lamb Inn, High Street, kept at the time of this photograph by John Blood, listed also as a coach proprietor.

Photographer – Unknown.   Source – Mrs Helena Steeples.

The present building was built in 1938 immediately behind the old pub. Part of the old building was left standing until the new one was complete, thus preserving the continuity of the liquor licence. The thin modern bricks, false timber framing and stained glass were straight out of a 'Brewer's Tudor' handbook, and the modern pub sign shows (imaginatively!) William Lamb, Viscount Melbourne, instead of a lamb.

Photographer – Thomas Tivey.   Source – Melbourne Photographic Society.

The Doves, pictured here, were blacksmiths and agricultural implement makers, a trade which was to develop with the gradual mechanisation of market gardening and the growth of private motoring. The site eventually became a garage, but the link with blacksmithing did not end until the 1960s when Henry Dove, grandson of the firm's founder, retired as the last working blacksmith.

Photographer – Unkown.

Source – Richard Heath.

The smithy is now Dove's Garage, a self-service petrol filling station and motor repair workshop. This progression of a family business from blacksmith to auto garage is not uncommon.

Photographer – Thomas Tivey.   Source – Melbourne Photographic Society.

However, Melbourne still has a village ▶ blacksmith. The picture shows Bill Smith in his Church Street smithy. He works in a traditional style, but no longer as a farrier. He is well known as a gatesmith, and examples of his work can be seen at several properties in the town.

Photographer – Peter Clough
Source – Melbourne Photographic Society.

The Star Tea Company was one of Melbourne's early chain stores, opened in Derby Road at the turn of the century. The photograph shows the display for the coronation celebrations of Edward VII and Queen Alexandra on June 27th 1902. The shop is perhaps best remembered by its customers just before its closure in 1965 for the friendly and efficient service under its manager Mr Copestake - a period when fresh-faced delivery boys negotiated the streets with large heavy bicycles with even larger overloaded carriers on the front. The projecting building on the left severely restricted the width of the road, and the whole group was demolished in order to widen Derby Road at its junction with Blanch Croft.

Photographer – Edward Martin.
Source – Melbourne Civic Society.

John Coton still provides a personal service from behind the counter in his grandmother's shop, Ward's ironmongers at 54 Derby Road. When this picture was taken in 1999 John would have sold you half a pound of nails and a dozen size eight screws wrapped up in old newspaper, but from January 1st 2000 he has had to change over to metric units. He says that 250 grams of nails doesn't sound right, but he'll still wrap them up in the same way.

Photographer – Thomas Tivey.
Source – Melbourne Photographic Society.

TRANSPORT AND COMMUNICATIONS

*"O*ld Thomas Taft" of Kings Newton died in 1861 in his 93rd year and was believed to be the oldest man in the parish at the time. He could remember when the Melbourne roads were knee deep in mud, the time when the first stage coach started, and when Melbourne produce was carried to Derby market on pack horses[36].

He did not live to see the coming of the railway to Melbourne in 1867, an event which had been eagerly awaited by the Melbourne tradesmen. Melbourne's favourable position on the communications network today is a threat as well as an advantage, as it has brought pressure for rapid change and expansion on a massive scale never seen before.

A very early photograph of a train standing in Melbourne Station, possibly taken in 1868 when the line opened to passenger traffic. Mr Shaw's station bus, which has called to collect passengers for the Melbourne Hotel, is clearly seen to the right of the picture in the station forecourt.

Photographer - Unknown.   Source - Bill James.

This photograph is believed to show excavations for bringing the railway to Melbourne, providing a service to and from Ashby-de-la-Zouch and Derby. The railway was blamed for closing Melbourne's weekly street market. It was during these excavations that a Saxon cremation cemetery was discovered between Kings Newton and the proposed railway station.

Photographer – Unknown.

Source – Richard Heath.

Melbourne railway station was opened by Thomas Cook, the pioneer of modern tourism, on Thursday, September 10th, 1868. It closed to passenger traffic in 1930, and during the Second World War it became part of the Melbourne and Kings Newton Military Railway. After the war the line carried limestone from the Breedon and Cloud Hill Quarries to the Sheffield steelmaking plants, finally closing in 1982. Today, all the station buildings have gone and scarcely anything remains except the crumbling remnants of the platforms.

Photographer – Edward Martin.

Source – Melbourne Civic Society.

The railway track is now part of an extensive network of cycle paths constructed by "Sustrans" (Sustainable Transport) Ltd., a charity based in Bristol. The National Cycle Network was chosen by the Millennium Commission in 1995 as a project of National importance to mark the year 2000. 3,000 miles will be complete by the year 2000, with a further 5,000 or 6,000 miles complete by 2005. This section, from Trent Lane to Worthington, was opened early in the 1990s, and is a popular recreational route at weekends, as the photograph shows.

Photographer – Thomas Tivey.

Source – Melbourne Photographic Society.

"To and from the Station" is written on the side of Mr Shaw's horse-drawn coach, but in practice it would have catered only for visitors and those able to afford to stay at the New Inn and Melbourne Arms (later the Melbourne Hotel). At the cost of a shilling, most locals would walk.

Photographer - Unknown.   Source - Richard Heath.

Melbourne's Post Office and Grocery Store, pictured here shortly before the present, larger premises were built on the same site by Joseph W. Warren in 1907. His great-grandfather Joseph Warren was appointed Postmaster in 1838; after his death in 1843 the position was held consecutively by his widow, son, grandson and great-grandson[37].

Photographer - Edward Martin.
Source - Melbourne Civic Society.

This grand Edwardian post office is little altered from the day that it was built, and is now run by Peter and Karen Ward.

Photographer - Peter Clough
Source - Melbourne Photographic Society.

This modern double-decker bus in the Market Place is the no. 68 Swadlincote to Derby service, holding ten times as many passengers as Mr Shaw's horse-drawn coach.

Photographer - Thomas Tivey.
Source - Melbourne Photographic Society.

THE STREET SCENE

Some of Melbourne's older streets have been subject to name changes. Church Street, here, was known as Back Street at the time of the photograph, and before that as Fennel Street. Showing on the left with trees in the playground is the infants department of the National School in nearby Penn Lane. It opened on September 1st 1884, with Miss Bushby as mistress in charge, and closed in 1952 when the new Infants School was built in Packhorse Road.

Photographer – Edward Martin.
Source – Melbourne Civic Society.

A deliberate re-creation of the previous scene permits many comparisons. The cottages on the right were demolished following a clearance order made in 1962[38]. The former Infants School on the left is now a learner swimming pool. The family car has replaced the horse and cart, and the child's pushchair can be folded so that it can fit into the car boot. In the centre of the picture the Old Brewery's bottle store has been demolished opening up a better view of the former brewer's house.

Photographer – Thomas Tivey.
Source – Melbourne Photographic Society.

A view of Castle Square looking south. The former Manor House (extreme left) was destroyed by fire in 1933 and was replaced by the simple Art Deco frontage of Castle Mills. This has in turn been replaced by a modern housing development which architecturally is undeserving of such a prominent location.

Photographer – Unknown.   Source – Melbourne Civic Society (Dashwood Fane Album).

The World War II bomb which demolished The Lodge at least opened up a fine view of the Parish Church from the southern end of Castle Square.

Photographer – Thomas Tivey.
Source – Melbourne Photographic Society.

Melbourne Market Place in 1897: people are gathering for Queen Victoria's Diamond Jubilee celebrations.

Photographer – Edward Martin.   Source – Melbourne Civic Society.

The Market Place and Derby Road are still the busiest part of Melbourne, now requiring the attention of a traffic warden.

Photographer – Thomas Tivey.   Source – Melbourne Photographic Society.

The Co-op, built by the Derby Co-operative Society and opened in 1915, is built in the Society's house style with dressings of glazed earthenware known as "faience". In the 1960s, in an ill-conceived effort to modernise the building, much of the faience work to the ground storey was ruthlessly hacked off to make way for a feeble and dreary new facing of painted matchboarding.

Local resident Mrs Janet Davison fortunately rescued one of the decorative blocks bearing the Society's monogram, and was pleased to allow a mould to be made from it when the faience was partially restored in 1998. The work was part funded by a conservation scheme which aided the repair of many historic buildings in Melbourne between 1992 and 1998. The Co-op's former status as Melbourne's largest shop was eclipsed by the opening of Budgens supermarket in 1996, but the Co-op has retained ownership of the building and now runs a travel agency there.

Photographer - Richard Lane.

Source - Melbourne Photographic Society.

The same scene at Christmas immediately prior to the restoration of the Co-op. Each year the large Christmas tree is donated by the Staunton Harold Estate and erected and lit by Melbourne Rotary Club. The small trees on the buildings are provided by the Parish Council, and strings of white lights across the streets were added by the Melbourne Business Association in 1999.

Photographer - Gavin Lake.

Source - Melbourne Photographic Society

Another view of the Market Place, this time looking west, and showing the monument built to commemorate Queen Victoria's Golden Jubilee. The construction of the monument was delayed, but the Derby Mercury of June 5th 1889 was at last able to report that "The monument in the Market Place is now nearly complete. On Saturday (1st) the builders finished the spire that surmounts it, having previously enclosed a large bottle containing a copy of the Jubilee Times (supplied by Mr. H H Crewe), a list of the subscribers, patterns of lace, leaflets of tradesmen, journals etc....".

Photographer - Edward Martin.   Source - Melbourne Civic Society.

Potter Street was the principal street of mediaeval Melbourne, and was still the most densely developed street as late as 1790. It is now full of parked cars, but the view is otherwise little changed.

Photographer – Edward Martin.
Source – Melbourne Civic Society.

This present-day view of Potter Street from Castle Square is dominated by parked cars in the Square itself and along both sides of the street. The cottages on the right are now fully renovated. In the foreground, immediately behind the two nearest cars, are the Reform Act Monument, moved from the Market Place in 1888, and a young oak tree replacing one planted by the Civic Society in 1994, which was vandalised.

Photographer – Mr H Rhodes.
Source – Melbourne Civic Society.

This view shows Russell Street, which once joined the Market Place to Derby Road. On the left is the Post Office and Savings Bank kept by the Warrens.

Photographer - Unknown.
Source - Richard Heath (Warren Album).

Russell Street is now part of Derby Road. The Melbourne Hotel stable yard, now a courtyard containing modern lock-up shops, adopted the name Russell Yard to keep the old name alive.

Photographer – Thomas Tivey.   Source – Melbourne Photographic Society.

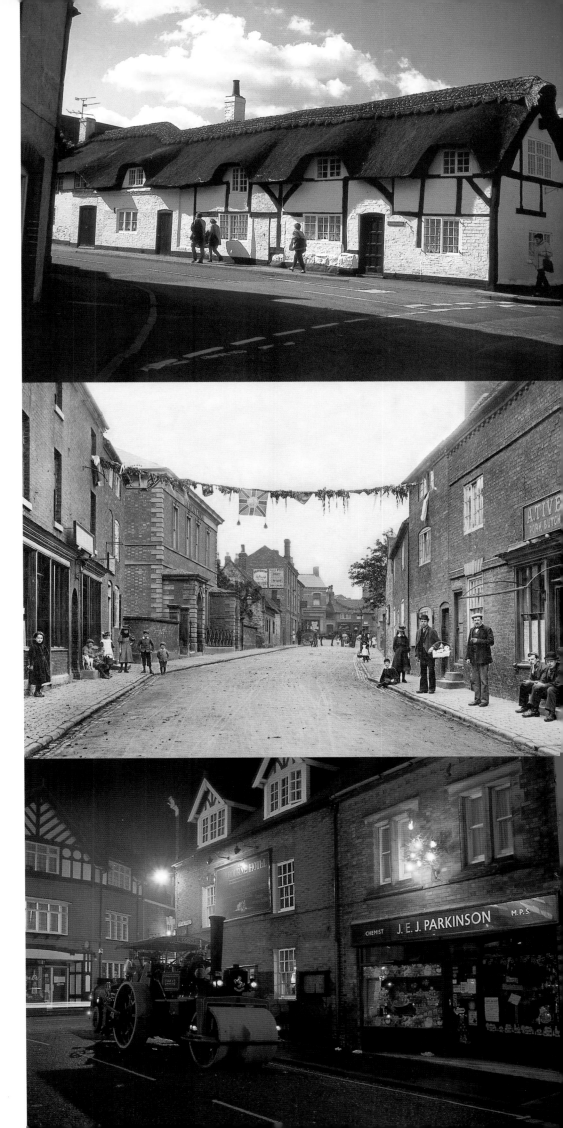

Another view of the 'Thatched Cottages', as the single family home is now called. Before their renovation, which took place in stages from 1965-72[39], Shardlow Rural District Council tried to persuade the owner to pull them down to make way for a three storey block of flats built across the angle! Fortunately, nothing became of the idea.

Photographer - Thomas Tivey.

Source - Melbourne Photographic Society.

Looking up Potter Street towards the Post Office: the decorations are for Queen Victoria's Diamond Jubilee in 1897. Centre left is the Mechanics' Institute or Athenaeum whose foundation stone was laid by Lord Palmerston in 1853.

Photographer - Edward Martin.

Source - John Parker.

This photograph was taken at the top end of Potter Street just before the Melbourne Business Association's late night shopping event in 1998: the vintage steamroller parked outside Parkinson's Chemist shop was one of the festive attractions.

Photographer - Gavin Lake.

Source - Melbourne Photographic Society.

A peaceful view of Kings Newton Main Street. Chantry House, on the left, is an old house but its present ostentatious appearance is the result of alterations in 1851 by Mr. Orton, a maltster and brickmaker. John Joseph Briggs recorded the work in his diary as follows:

"Mr. Orton who purchased Mrs. Archer's (late Nicklinson's) property has altered the house in Newton standing upon it. He has raised the roof - made pointed gables - put in windows and made it Elizabethan in character. It has cost about £250 - the plans were by Stevens of Derby"[40]

The other buildings in the photograph all still exist, but the roofs have all been raised and replaced with tiles. The lime trees in the background appear to have been planted in 1856[41], and by the time of this photograph had grown large enough to enhance the view.

Photographer - Edward Martin.

Source - Melbourne Civic Society.

The thatched cottages in Main Street were re-roofed early in the 20th century. The large gabled dormers were added at the same time, and are a characteristic feature of several houses in the village.

Photographer - Marshall Payne.

Source - Melbourne Photographic Society.

Another attractive group of black and white buildings. The Hardinge Arms in the foreground was formerly a beer shop and the 'home' of the Newton Wonder apple. It is now a large public house with a function suite and accommodation. Beyond is Four Gables, formerly the Gayborder Nurseries, famed for its Michaelmas Daisies.

Photographer - Thomas Tivey.

Source - Melbourne Photographic Society.

This view of the Cross at Kings Newton is from Trent Lane, formerly Marsh Lane, showing the Georgian house known as "Cofton". Growing from the steps of the mediaeval Cross is a lime tree planted by Thomas Scott around 1777. It was replaced by the present cross erected to commemorate Edward VIII, the King who was never crowned, in 1936.

Photographer – Edward Martin.
Source – Melbourne Civic Society.

Another view of "Cofton", showing the commemorative cross and the bollards recently installed by the Kings Newton Residents Association to prevent further damage to the cross plinth by heavy lorries.

Photographer – Thomas Tivey.
Source – Melbourne Photographic Society.

The inscription on the commemorative cross at Kings Newton.

Photographer – Thomas Tivey.
Source – Melbourne Photographic Society.

HERE STOOD THE ANCIENT CROSS OF
KINGS NEWTON
THIS ONE WAS ERECTED TO MARK
THE ACCESSION TO THE THRONE OF
HIS MAJESTY KING EDWARD VIII
AD 1936

A view of High Street showing, on the left, Dallman's the pork butchers and the Cruck Cottage. On the right is Mr Springthorpe in his tea shop or, as printed on the window, "refreshment rooms". The porch next door belongs to Bank House where James Earp in 1874 opened Melbourne's first bank[42].

Photographer – Edward Martin.   Source – Melbourne Civic Society.

The former tea shop is now an antiques and carpet shop, and the Bank House is a private dwelling. Although little else has changed, a close inspection of these two photographs shows that the roads are now much cleaner - and less smelly!

Photographer – Thomas Tivey.   Source – Melbourne Photographic Society.

A view over Melbourne looking north-west from the church tower, about 1893. At first glance this looks like a rural scene, with a farmyard and the blacksmith's house and forge in the foreground. But after a close inspection the picture gives a more urban impression. It shows four nonconformist chapels, several factories, and the tower of the Athenaeum in the centre on the horizon. To its right, Coxon's factory on Victoria Street is just visible, and further to the right are the chimneys of Joseph Bullock's joinery works and Kendrick Mill.

Photographer – Edward Martin.   Source – Melbourne Civic Society (Dashwood Fane Album).

The Church or National School in Penn Lane. The school was built on the site of the Lady Elizabeth Hastings Charity School in 1821-2, largely due to the efforts of parish curate James Bagge. Looking at the numbers of children in the photograph it is hard to believe that so many children could be accommodated.

Photographer – Edward Martin.

Source – Melbourne Civic Society.

In 1969, upon the opening of the new Junior School on Packhorse Road, the National School became an annexe to the Secondary Modern School (the former Board School) on High Street. It finally closed in 1977 when Melbourne's Secondary School pupils were transferred to the newly-built Comprehensive School at Chellaston, and was sold shortly afterwards. The building was repaired with financial help from the Melbourne conservation scheme, and is currently undergoing an imaginative and sensitive conversion into two flats.

Photographer – Chris Brown.   Source – Melbourne Photographic Society.

The Public Hall and Liberal Club in Derby Road, possibly taken upon its completion. The foundation stones were laid in 1889 by Henry Wardle, MP for the Southern Division of Derbyshire, and local businessman Edmund Salsbury, and it was built at a cost of £1200, which included the caretaker's apartments[43].

Photographer – Unknown.

Source – Richard Heath.

The Public Hall and Liberal Club looks very different today because in 1970 the whole of the front was reinforced and refaced due to the structural failure of the original façade [44].

Photographer – Thomas Tivey.

Source – Melbourne Photographic Society.

Segregation of the sexes was the order of the day when John "Gaffer" Wright became headmaster of the newly-built Board School in High Street in 1897. Before that date the children of dissenters or nonconformists were taught in rented buildings, the boys under Mr Wright in the Baptist schoolrooms in Chapel Street and the infants and girls under Miss Wilkes in the Athenaeum in Potter Street.

Before the 1902 Education Act the elected School Board held its meetings in the fine panelled room at first floor level which subsequently - until 1999 - served as the chamber of the Parish Council. The School closed in 1977 to become the Leisure Centre, later re-named the Bill Shone Leisure Centre following the death of its much-respected last headmaster. Apart from the removal of the dividing railings and the use of the playground as a car park the building is little altered.

Photographer - Edward Martin.   Source - Melbourne Civic Society.

The new Junior School in Packhorse Road, opened in 1969, used CLASP (Consortium of Local Authorities Special Projects) pre-fabricated components, and is typical of many schools built in the Midlands at that time. It forms part of Melbourne's educational campus, and has extensive grass and hard playing fields, unlike the school it replaced.

Photographer - Thomas Tivey.   Source - Melbourne Photographic Society.

Children and parents leaving the two primary schools (Junior and Infants) passing the third building on the campus which houses the youth club, playgroups and adult education.

Photographer - Thomas Tivey.

Source - Melbourne Photographic Society.

The Thomas Cook Memorial Cottages opened during a week of celebrations[45], commencing Monday, March 9th 1891 with a devotional meeting in the Mission Hall, followed on the Tuesday by the presentation of the Deed of Trust, a dinner at the Melbourne Hotel for the trustees, and lunch for invited guests in the Mission Hall, followed by an afternoon's inspection of the Memorial buildings. The week ended on Sunday with a service in the Mission Hall. The allotment of cottages was made in the following week.

Photographer - Edward Martin.
Source - Melbourne Civic Society.

The Thomas Cook Memorial Cottages still operate under the original Deed of Trust controlled by twelve trustees. They were extensively modernised over a 20 year period, culminating in the refurbishment of the Mission Hall in 1996 and the addition of a new bungalow at the side.

Photographer - Thomas Tivey.
Source - Melbourne Photographic Society.

The local trustees and residents of the Thomas Cook Memorial Cottages in 1892, a year after they were opened. At that time the rule was that "..no cottage shall be occupied by more than four persons at one time" and the rent was one penny per week per person!

Photographer - Edward Martin.
Source - Ernie Beardsley

The Constabulary, shown here, was built next to the site of the town's pinfold on Turnbarrel in 1893-4[46], complete with lock-up cells and a small exercise yard, the latter now gone and replaced with a private house. The constabulary itself is also now a private house.

Melbourne's lock-up or roundhouse originally stood close to the Roebuck Inn in Potter Street, built shortly after a court order was issued in 1790 stating that all parishes in the county should provide a "place of temporary confinement for the reception of vagrants and paupers who had either returned to their own parish or were en route to their place of settlement". It was no longer used for this purpose after the formation of the Poor Law Union in 1835, when the responsibility was transferred to Shardlow. The last reference to the lock-up was in 1870, shortly before its demolition, on a bill of sale mentioning "that building formerly used as a roundhouse, but now used as a coalhouse".

Photographer - Edward Martin.   Source - Richard Heath.

SOME MELBOURNE HOUSES

The façade of Pool Cottage must be the most ornate domestic frontage anywhere in Melbourne. It was built as an extension to the miller's house in 1839[47] and was part of an extensive programme of improvements to the Pool in the 1830s and '40s. The old part of the house, timber framed and thatched, was rebuilt in 1933[48]. In the low stone kerbing alongside the Pool, two rectangular notches mark the spot where two young girls were blown into the pool and drowned. They were on their way to feed the cats at the mill during a dark and stormy evening in 1884. When a search was made for them, the first discovery was of the mill key, lying at the bottom of the pool where the notches were later cut[49].

Photographer - Edward Martin.

Source - Melbourne Civic Society.

Pool Cottage is now a residential home for the elderly, run by David and Hilary Bellaby. The small stone-roofed structure in the foreground controls the water flow to three of the fountains in Melbourne Hall Gardens.

Photographer - Thomas Tivey.

Source - Melbourne Photographic Society.

Melbourne Hall was originally a mediaeval rectory. The house as we see it today is mostly the result of three major building programmes by the Coke family in 1629-31, 1725-7 and 1742-5, but the shape and layout of the mediaeval house is still echoed in the present arrangement and the house has a powerful atmosphere of antiquity and stability. This view shows the south front overlooking the Pool. The stucco has now been removed, the railings have gone, and the small conservatory was replaced by a larger structure in 1911.

Photographer – Unknown.

Source – Melbourne Civic Society (Dashwood Fane Album).

Melbourne Hall and gardens looking west, with the principal front in the background. The Hall is probably best known for its gardens, laid out by Vice Chamberlain Thomas Coke in 1704 with assistance from the Royal Gardeners Messrs. London and Wise. This view shows the path down the centre of the formal parterre garden, with the house oddly off-centre due to the historical constraints of the site. In the foreground is the top of the wrought iron summerhouse known as the Birdcage, made at Melbourne in 1706-8 by the famous ironsmith Robert Bakewell.

Photographer – Thomas Tivey.

As far as is known, Kings Newton Hall was never photographed before its dramatic destruction by fire one night in April 1859. Formerly the home of the Hardy (later Harding) family, it became part of the Melbourne estate in 1734 and was occupied by a series of gentleman tenants. The unfortunate tenant in 1859 was Mr Green, who held a sale of his remaining goods after the fire and left Melbourne.

Lady Palmerston decided against rebuilding the house, and the £2000 insurance money was spent elsewhere. The Hall stood in ruins for fifty years, and by the end of the century much of the stonework was covered in a dense growth of ivy. This picture shows the ruins shortly after the fire.

Photographer – Unknown.

Source – Melbourne Civic Society (Dashwood Fane Album).

In 1909-10 the ruined Hall was purchased and very carefully restored by Sir Cecil Paget, General Superintendent (and later Chairman) of the Midland Railway. Despite the many years of dereliction, much of the stonework remained sound and was carefully consolidated. The interior of the building is entirely new, but substantial parts of the exterior, including the four main gables, are largely original. This undated view of the main entrance gates appears to have been taken shortly after reconstruction had been completed.

Photographer – Unknown.

Source – Philip Heath.

Chantry House on Church Street in Melbourne was originally a possession of St. Katherine's Chantry, founded in Melbourne Church by William Bars of King's Newton in 1380. In 1725 the house was purchased and rebuilt by Samuel Shepherdson of Derby, a gentleman farmer whose activities also extended to brickmaking, building and malting[50]. In 1799 it was purchased by his great grandson Henry Fox, agent to the Melbourne Estate[51], and the garden front shown here probably dates from that time. A proposal to build a housing estate in the grounds of Chantry House led to the formation of the Melbourne Civic Society in 1974. The house was subsequently purchased and restored by Ronald Loake.

Photographer - Unknown.

Source - Courtesy of Derby Local Studies Library.

Reference to Chantry House in Kings Newton has already been made (see page 58). Another interesting episode in its history relates to the old custom of "plough-bullocking" on "Plough Monday", which was the day when farming communities returned to their labours after the Christmas season. Six or eight men would be harnessed in pairs to an ordinary plough under the charge of a driver with a long whip. The plough was dragged along the roads with a lot of rough play, and money was asked from various houses en route to fund a drinking session at the end.

If money was refused, the gang would threaten to tear up the pavement or "causeway" in front of the offending property, and this actually happened at Chantry House sometime before the 1850s. Mr Nicklinson, the owner at the time, refused to give anything, so the order was given to "plough up" and the pavement was destroyed. In the light of this tale, the present survival of the old red brick pavement outside Chantry House may be seen as a piece of poetic justice[52].

Photographer - Thomas Tivey.   Source - Melbourne Photographic Society.

"Vale House" on Penn Lane was originally a farm building, backing onto the large farmyard belonging to the Dower House. It was rebuilt as a house by William Scott in 1814, but some of the old walling was left standing and ventilation slits can still be seen in the east gable, a survival from when it was a farm building. The view towards Vale House, framed by the winding stone walls enclosing Penn Lane, is one of Melbourne's most satisfying pieces of townscape[53].

Photographer - Edward Martin.   Source - Melbourne Civic Society.

Vale House, now the home of
Vernon and Kath Kington,
is as pretty as ever,
as this recent photograph shows.

Photographer - Thomas Tivey.

Source - Melbourne Photographic Society.

"Rose Cottage" on Penn Lane, despite its cosy domestic appearance, is actually an early barn conversion. It was built around 1800 as a coach house and cheese chambers, and a survey of 1808 noted that it was the only building on the whole farm that was of any quality. It was converted to a house in 1868, when the farmland was dispersed and the old farmhouse pulled down. The render on the front of the building conceals the timber lintels above the former coach house doors[54].

Photographer – Edward Martin.
Source – Melbourne Civic Society.

Rose Cottage today lives up to its name: the garden is a quintessential English cottage garden.

Photographer – Thomas Tivey.
Source – Melbourne Photographic Society.

Except for Blanch Croft, the new streets of Melbourne laid out during the Industrial Revolution have all been redeveloped. They were never properly studied or recorded, and photographic coverage of them is very poor. This photograph shows part of Pingle Cottages, an attractive range of early 19th century houses whose demolition is still lamented by many Melbourne people. The Pingle as it exists today is a modern housing development designed by D.R. and D.W. Variava of Eastwood in 1969[55].

Photographer – Unknown..
Source – Philip Heath.

The terrace in the centre of the picture is nos. 20-24 Ashby Road, called "Aroma Villas". The name was deliberately humorous, as the three houses were built in 1884 by William Cook, wholesale and retail tobacconist of Havana House, South Street, who also bottled ale and porter. No. 20, the house at the right end of Aroma Villas, was where photographer Edward Martin had his home and studio[56]. These Victorian middle-class villas were well-built and spacious. Indeed, the rooms are larger and higher than those in some of the modern housing recently constructed in the town.

Photographer – Thomas Tivey.   Source – Melbourne Photographic Society.

Most Victorian terraced houses were built for renting. These modern homes in Oaklands Way were built in the 1980s for owner-occupation. They are detached, centrally heated, with a garage and parking space and front and back gardens. Separatism is the rule, and the idea of putting two front doors side by side as in the photograph of the cottages at The Pingle (page 68 opposite, below) would be unpopular with most house builders today.

Photographer – Thomas Tivey.   Source – Melbourne Photographic Society.

"Vale Cottage", like the adjoining Vale House, was once part of the extensive range of farm buildings belonging to the Dower House. The garden shown here was once part of the farmyard.

Photographer – Edward Martin.
Source – Melbourne Civic Society.

Jeffrey and Laura Jones have lived at Vale Cottage since 1993 and have created a fine modern garden which respects the historic setting. The window visible in the extreme top right of the photograph shows that part of the adjoining barn has been incorporated into the house. The rest of the barn is Gale's motor repair garage.

Photographer – Ken Leech.
Source – Melbourne Photographic Society.

The garden of Castle Farm, the home of John and Jackie Blunt, showing the ivy clad remains of the castle, on a day when it was open to the public under the National Gardens Scheme.

Photographer – Thomas Tivey.
Source – Melbourne Photographic Society.

CELEBRATIONS, LEISURE AND SPECIAL OCCASIONS

The Melbourne Ladies' Cycle Club, assembled in the Market Place in 1897 before taking their place in the parade to celebrate Queen Victoria's Diamond Jubilee. Cycling was a rapidly growing hobby in the last years of the nineteenth century, and the cycles are decorated in ribbons and flowers.

Photographer – Edward Martin.

Source – Harold Pipes.

Today we decorate lorries in the same way. This picture was taken from the bedroom window of 23 Market Place (courtesy of Mark Watson and Serena Krzyckowska), and shows one of Joe Laban's lorries carrying the Staunton Women's Institute float in the 1999 Carnival parade. Edward Martin's photograph (left) was probably taken from the very same room.

Apart from the shopfronts, many of the buildings are the same, and it looks as though the banners in both pictures are fixed in the same place. The clock in this photograph was put up in 1949/50, but had not worked since the early 1990s. It was replaced in December 1999 through the efforts of the Millennium Committee, in readiness for taking Melbourne into the year 2000.

Photographer – Gavin Lake.   Source – Melbourne Photographic Society.

A typical Melbourne Harvest Festival in the former Congregational Chapel (now United Reformed) in High Street.

Photographer – W Mayell.

Source – Philip Heath.

The 1999 Harvest Festival at Melbourne Baptist Chapel, with the Reverend Kenneth Green in the pulpit and Ernest Beardsley at the organ.

The first chapel was built on the site in 1749-50. It was enlarged as early as 1768, and subsequently altered on numerous occasions. In 1760 Thomas Perkins came to Melbourne to be ordained as joint minister with local man Francis Smith. Thomas was the grandfather of Thomas Cook who, before becoming the 'Founder of Modern Tourism', was an active evangelist. The method he adopted to develop his ability to speak in public was to climb through the chapel window, with his lifelong friend John Earp, in the early hours of the morning and each in turn become preacher and congregation.

Photographer – Thomas Tivey.

Source – Melbourne Photographic Society.

A pause outside the Roebuck for an Edward Martin photograph. The occasion is not recorded but was perhaps the Coronation of George V, as Arthur Haines was landlord at the Roebuck during the 1910s. This splendid turnout belongs to Arthur Cartlidge and his family.

Photographer – Edward Martin.

Source – Mrs Winifred Taylor.

The Staunton Women's Institute float being judged at the start of the Carnival parade showing (left to right) Shirley Edwards behind the balloon, Sue Hand with the maracas, and Pat Smith, Margaret Wright and Annie Gidlow on the steel drums. They won joint first prize for their display.

Photographer – Chris Brown.

Source – Melbourne Photographic Society.

In Melbourne, whatever the celebration, it was customary to end with a bun-fight. This occasion was probably the Queen's Diamond Jubilee in 1897 when the venue was a large marquee in King's Field by Melbourne Pool.

Photographer – Edward Martin.

Source – Philip Heath.

Today, the town's celebrations often end on the Junior School playing field with beer, skittles and balloons.

Photographer – Chris Brown.

Source – Melbourne Photographic Society.

WAKES MELBOURNE. E. MARTIN.

▲
The annual Wakes Week and Statutes, shown here in the Market Place. It was moved to its present site in Castle Square in 1904 when it was still a hiring fair. Strong young men of 18 to 20 years were offered situations at about £18 per annum and those of 12 to 16 years £10 to £16 with board and lodgings. Today, the event is marked only by a funfair which takes place shortly after Michaelmas (September 29th), St. Michael being one of the patron saints of the Parish Church.

Melbourne once had an annual fair for the sale of goods etc., originally established by a Royal Charter of 1230 granted to Walter, Bishop of Carlisle, but it was discontinued by the late 16th century.

Photographer – Edward Martin.
Source – Melbourne Civic Society.

▶
These three young ladies are the two Slater sisters with an unidentified companion, photographed in Edward Martin's Ashby Road studio. They are dressed à la mode for an occasion, with hats, gloves and flower sprays.

Photographer – Edward Martin.
Source – Melbourne Civic Society.

The Holland family from Mountsorrel have for generations brought the Wakes fair to Melbourne. Amusements and fast food are now the order of the day, but there is still a helter-skelter for the little children and sideshows for those of us who never grow up.

Photographer – Thomas Tivey.

Source – Melbourne Photographic Society.

These three young ladies, Louise standing and Gemma and Sophie seated, were photgraphed in Thomas Tivey's Victoria Street studio in 1999 before going to a party. They, too, are dressed for the occasion.

Photographer – Thomas Tivey.

Source – Melbourne Photographic Society.

A photograph of the Ward family, members of which manufactured cardboard boxes to supply the boot and shoe industry of Melbourne. Also in the picture, on the left with his bicycle, is in-law Arthur Hair of Hair's Brewery, Church Street, and his family.

Photographer – Edward Martin.

Source – Richard Heath.

Three generations of the Heath family, who have lived and worked at Woodhouse Farm, Woodhouses, since 1959.

Photographer – Peter Clough.

Source – Melbourne Photographic Society.

The wedding of Mr and Mrs William Frearson in 1901. Both were lifelong
Methodists, and in 1932 William wrote a history of Methodism in Melbourne.
He was also one of the trustees responsible for the Methodists' acquisition of the
Athenaeum on Potter Street in the 1940s, and its development under the new
name "Wesley Hall".

Photographer – Edward Martin.

Source – Melbourne Civic Society.

The Cooper family at the wedding of Lydia Cooper and Ian Timson on 26th of
June 1999, photographed outside Melbourne Hall.

Photographer – Peter Clough

Melbourne Town Band in the Hall Gardens. Melbourne had a town band as early as September 1845 when they played on one of the new islands in Melbourne Pool to celebrate Lord Melbourne's arrival at the Hall. In 1856 they played "in their best style" to celebrate the end of the Crimean War and in 1860 they were commended at the great National Brass Band Contest at Crystal Palace.

During the Crimean War, the band had been carried away by military enthusiasm and answered an advertisement in the "Times" seeking a band to accompany a ship's crew to the Baltic. The ship's chaplain came to engage them, offering rations, clothing and £80 a man for two years. By this time the enthusiasm had cooled, and after consultation with wives and sweethearts the offer was declined[57].

Photographer – Edward Martin.

Source – Melbourne Civic Society.

An unidentified group of businessmen. It is thought that they may be members of the Melbourne Prosecution of Felons Society, founded in 1790 to help preserve law and order. When the police force was established it became a social gathering, finally fading away with the outbreak of the First World War.

Photographer – Edward Martin.

Source – Richard Heath.

Melbourne Rotary Club at their weekly meeting in Melbourne Hall Tea Rooms, with President Cliff Haynes.

Photographer – Thomas Tivey.

Source – Melbourne Photographic Society.

The 1999 Melbourne Town Band in the grounds of the Baptist Chapel off Derby Road: the most noticeable difference, of course, is that the band is now mixed.

Photographer – Thomas Tivey.

Source – Melbourne Photographic Society.

The Parish Church Choir around the turn of the century in the vicarage garden - strictly a men and boys situation in those days.

Photographer – Edward Martin.

Source – Richard Heath.

Today, like the Town Band, the church choir is mixed. They were photographed here just before the retirement of
Canon Frederick Ross, vicar of Melbourne, in 1998.

Photographer – Stanyard Photography.

A village cricket match in progress at the Melbourne Recreation Ground.   Photographer – Thomas Tivey.   Source – Melbourne Photographic Society.

Melbourne Church

Photographer – Chris Brown.   Source – Melbourne Photographic Society.

Out with the Old and in with the New! The Melbourne bells are rung from the floor because a ringing chamber would obscure the fine view up the tower. The bellringing team rang in the New Millennium, and are seen here practising for the induction of the new vicar.

Photographer – Thomas Tivey.   Source – Melbourne Photographic Society.

Abbreviations.

Briggs MS	Manuscript History of Melbourne 1820-1875, in the form of a diary, by John Joseph Briggs. Derby Local Studies Library, manuscript no. 4607.
DRO	The Derbyshire County Record Office.
HL	The Huntington Library, San Marino, California, USA.
LeicsRO	The Leicestershire County Record Office.
LichRO	The Lichfield Record Office, Lichfield, Staffordshire.
MHMR	Melbourne Hall Muniment Room.
PRO	The Public Record Office, London.
SDDC	South Derbyshire District Council, Civic Offices, Swadlincote.

Footnotes to text of "A Short History of Melbourne"

1   From a newspaper article in a scrapbook compiled by William Garratt, agent at Melbourne Hall. DRO D825 Z/Z1. (Melbourne Australia had a population of 314 in 1836, rising to 130,000 by 1869).

2   Palmer and Neaverson "Industrial Landscapes of the East Midlands", Phillimore 1992.

3   MHMR Estate Accounts.

4   Philip Zeigler "Melbourne: A biography of William Lamb, 2nd Viscount Melbourne", Fontana/Collins 1978, page 81.

5   Briggs MS, page 63.

6   Scrapbook of William Garratt, Derbyshire Record Office D825 Z/Z1.

7   MHMR Estate Survey, 1808. LeicsRO DE500/29/1 (Rental of the Hastings estate in Melbourne, 1808) DRO D2375M: Plan and survey of Calke and Calke Park c1800; 63/54/5; 148/11; three letters dated 1789 in 32/13; 282/7/1; 67/64; 63/56; 67/47. DRO Melbourne Enclosure Award, 1791. DRO D73 (Cantrell of Kings Newton - includes rentals of the estate).

8   "Melbourne Church, Derbyshire". Text of a paper given at the British Archaeological Association Annual Conference, 1987, by Richard Gem.

9   Nikolaus Pevsner "The Buildings of England: Derbyshire", 2nd edition, revised by Elizabeth Williamson. Penguin Books, 1993.

10   DRO D2375M 53/5/9.

11   DRO D2375M 53/5/10. PRO DL44/560.

12   MHMR Box 11 Bundle 11.

13   MHMR 13/3/12 and 13.

14   DRO Melbourne Enclosure Award.

15   Introduction to A.S.Jacques "History of Melbourne", 1933. "Lady Matilda Holland, Henry of Lancaster and the Manor of Melbourne" by Joe W. Leedom in the *American Journal of Legal History* Volume 31, pp118-125.

16   PRO State Papers Domestic SP12-163.

17   LichRO Will of William Haimes of Melbourne, 1854 (probate granted 1855). This is the only document I have so far seen which actually calls the house "the Manor House".

18   MHMR 11/7/2a.

19   MHMR Box 240. Disbursements August 1636 - January 1636/7. The mill seems to have gone out of use by 1703, when the blackstones were removed from it for use at Melbourne Mill (MHMR Letter from J. Fisher to T. Coke 2/10/1703 Box 259 Bundle 15; Letter from R. Hardinge to T. Coke 6/12/1703 Box 259 Bundle 10).

20   The 1583 survey of Melbourne Castle (PRO State Papers Domestic) noted very great woods at Melbourne, but by 1623 they had gone (see LeicsRO DE658/8: response of jurors to the 6th article, and "addiconall nootes and abreviacons" on folio 105).

21   Petition against the warren 1733, in parish pamphlets box at Derbyshire Record Office; The Derby Mercury, October 12th to 19th, 1750.

22   DRO D3174/2.

23   MHMR Estate Survey, 1808.

24   HL Hastings Collection HAM 55/19, 22 and 23 MHMR Box 219, Folder "Melbourne Gardens 1698-1706".

25   Briggs MS, pages 2-3.

26   Briggs MS, page 90.

27   Title deeds to property on the corner of High Street and New Yard (now Thomas Cook Close), in the possession of the author.

28   Title deeds to nos. 33 and 35 Derby Road (in custody of H. Pipes & Co., Solicitors, Melbourne), and title deeds to No. 52, Blanch Croft, kept by Mr. John Robinson, owner of the property.

29   DRO D73/10.

30   Pilkington, James "A View of the Present State of Derbyshire" 1789, pp81-83.

31   HL HAD2243.

32   MHMR Parish Plan and Survey, 1840.

33   Briggs MS, pages 49 and 78.

34   Briggs MS, page 6.

35   Briggs MS, page 255.

36   DRO D825 Z/Z1.

37   LichRO Probate documents of John Robinson of Melbourne, 1761.

38   Account of the executors of the will of James Salsbury, in possession of Mr. G. E. Cook, Kings Newton Fields.

39   "A Tour in the Midlands 1789" in *The Torrington Diaries*, Eyre and Spottiswoode, 1935.

40   Pigot's Directory of Derbyshire, 1821/2; Bagshaw's Directory of Derbyshire 1846, and White's Directory of Derbyshire, 1857.

41   See, for example, the arguments about education in Melbourne in W. Garratt's scrapbook (DRO D825 Z/Z1).

42   The Derby Mercury, 18th May, 1864.

43   The Derby Reporter, 10th June, 1870.

44   MHMR Estate Accounts.

45   DRO D825 Z/Z1.

46   Briggs MS, page 76.

47   The Derby Reporter, June 8th, 1877.

48   A collection of these is owned by Mrs. Margaret Jackson of Kings Newton.

49   The 1891 Census Returns list Edward Martin, Photographer, living on Ashby Road.

50   The Derby Mercury, April 29th, 1921.

Footnotes to the Captions:

Captions written by Philip Heath and Richard Heath and jointly by the project team.

1   HL Hastings Manuscripts HA2420

        (Letter from John Earp to Earl Moira 31st October, 1810).

2   MHMR Estate Accounts 1834-40.

3   The Derbyshire Advertiser, 1873.

4   MHMR Estate Accounts; Survey of Melbourne Estate 1808.

5   Derby Evening Telegraph, 13th September, 1963.

6   "Tree-ring analysis of timbers from the Thatched Cottage, High Street, Melbourne, Derbyshire".
        University of Nottingham Tree-Ring Dating Laboratory Report, 1996.

7   MHMR Box 268 Bundle 344 part 1 items 1-14; Estate Accounts; LichRO Probate records of William Carter of Melbourne, 1823.

8   "Roods, Screens and Lofts in Derbyshire Churches" by Aymer Vallance FSA in *Memorials of Old Derbyshire* edited by Rev. J. C. Cox, 1907; History and Guide to Melbourne Church by R. J. Barman (1960), page 40.

9   MHMR Estate Accounts 1890.

10   MHMR Estate Accounts 1903.

11   The dating is based on the fact that the photograph shows the old Methodist Chapel in the distance with its roof at the original height. It was raised in 1884 (see Jacques History of Melbourne, 1933, page 101).

12   Lich RO Probate documents of William Cook of Melbourne (1703); MHMR Box 267 Bundle B344m Title deeds to Close House.

13   MHMR Deduced from various surveys and rentals.

14   MHMR Survey of the Melbourne Estate, 1808.

15   The Derby Mercury, 3rd September, 1926.

16   MHMR Estate Accounts 1797-8.

17   The Derby Mercury, 21st January, 1846.

18   It is shown as "disused" on the 1st edition 25" Ordnance Survey, published in 1887 but surveyed in 1882.

19   Derby Evening Telegraph 29th August, 1963.

20   Pieces of polished stone masonry, the same as can be seen in the remains of the castle, can still be seen at the mill, used for quoins and occasionally in the rubble walling. A letter from Sir John Coke the Elder to Sir John Coke the Younger refers to the Earl of Huntingdon's new mill at Melbourne (British Library, Add. mss. 69870, 25th June, 1638).

21   MHMR Estate Accounts 1832-3.

22   Derby Evening Telegraph 3rd October, 1968.

23   SDDC planning file ref: 871/123.

24   Derby Evening Telegraph 8th September, 1955.

25   Lease to Mander and Weaman 1726, recorded in a small collection of Melbourne Manorial material recently discovered at the offices of Seviers Solicitors, St. Mary's Gate Derby, and catalogued by Howard Usher, Melbourne.

26   Lloyd, Humphrey: "The Quaker Lloyds in the Industrial Revolution" Hutchinson, 1975, page 146.

27   HL Hastings collection (correspondence) HA2109.

28   MHMR Estate Accounts 1790.

29   Historical Metallurgy Group Bulletin No. 3, 1964; Private correspondence between Philip Heath and Mrs. Ann Lardeur of Chaldon, Surrey (daughter of Mr. W. H. Bailey who excavated the furnace).

30   MHMR Estate Accounts 1884; MHMR Box 169 correspondence and poster advertising sale of Charles Gregory's goods.

31   A. S. Jacques "History of Melbourne" (1933), pages 93-4.

32   DRO D2375M (Harpur Crewe). Household vouchers, 1919 (Bill heading of Edward Thompson).

33   Derby Local Studies Library Deed Collection, no. 2808 (Abstract of title of Joseph Bullock to a piece of land at Melbourne, 1884).

34   Derby Mercury, March 11th, 1921.

35   Abstract of Title to No. 26, Derby Road, 1926. In custody of H.Pipes and Co., Solicitors, Melbourne.

36   Briggs MS. pp258-259.

37   The Derby Mercury, 18th February, 1921.

38   The Derbyshire Advertiser, 22nd December, 1961 and 20th April, 1962.

39   South Derbyshire District Council planning files 764/127, 865/159 and 571/130.

40   Briggs MS. p49.

41   Briggs MS. pp106, 107 and 113.

42   A. S. Jacques "History of Melbourne" (1933) page 112.

43   A. S. Jacques "History of Melbourne" (1933) page 107.

44   SDDC planning files ref: 370/119.

45   Pamphlet entitled "Opening of the General Baptist Memorial Cottages and Mission Hall at Melbourne 1891" in possession of Richard Heath, Melbourne.

46   Copy local authority land sale deeds in possession of Richard Heath, Melbourne.

47   MHMR Estate Accounts 1839.

48   MHMR File "Estate Repairs and New Buildings 1932-1957".

49   Information from Mrs. E. M. Warren (née Adcock). See also the gravestone of the two girls in the Packhorse Road Cemetery.

50   MHMR 151/3 (Notebook of Samuel Shepherdson), page 17.

51   MHMR Box l0, Bundle 11; MHMR Box 169/4/4;27.

52   The Derby Mercury, 18th February, 1921.

53   MHMR Box 265 Bundle 343u.

54   MHMR Estate Accounts; MHMR Survey of Estate, 1808.

55   SDDC planning files ref: SEDRDC 169/132.

56   Information from Mrs. E.M. Warren (née Adcock) who lived at No. 18 Ashby Road when Edward Martin lived at No. 20.

57   The Derby Mercury, 18th February, 1921; Briggs MS. pp15, 93 and 110.

Casseroles
STEWS, HOTPOTS & HEARTY SOUPS

COMPILED BY
JENNENE PLUMMER

BayBooks
An imprint of HarperCollins*Publishers*

STOCKISTS

Home and Garden on the Mall
208 Level 2 Skygarden
Pitt Street
Sydney
Tel: (02) 235 1595

Les Olivades
2 Transvaal Ave
Double Bay
Tel: (02) 327 8073

Made on Earth
306 Mid City Centre
Sydney
Tel: (02) 223 2435

Corso de Fiori
35 South Dowling Street
Darlinghurst NSW
Tel: (02) 360 5151
(also Surry Hills, Chatswood,
Skygardens and Melbourne)

A BAY BOOKS PUBLICATION
An imprint of HarperCollinsPublishers

First published in 1993 in Australia by Bay Books

Bay Books, of
CollinsAngus&Robertson Publishers Pty Limited (ACN 009 913 517)
A division of HarperCollinsPublishers (Australia) Pty Limited
25 Ryde Road, Pymble NSW 2073, Australia

HarperCollinsPublishers (New Zealand) Limited
31 View Road, Glenfield, Auckland 10, New Zealand

HarperCollinsPublishers Limited
77-85 Fulham Palace Road, London W6 8JB, United Kingdom

Copyright © Bay Books 1993

National Library of Australia
Cataloguing-in-Publication data:

   Plummer, Jennene
   Casseroles, stews, hotpots and hearty soups.
      Includes index.
      ISBN 1 86378 069 6.

      1. Casserole cookery. 2. Stews. 3. Soups.
      I. Title.(Series: Bay Books cookery collection)
   641.8

Chapter opener and front cover photography by Rowan Fotheringham
Food Stylist: Carolyn Fienberg
Food Stylist's Assistants: Joanne Forest, Jody Vassallo
Food Editor: Jennene Plummer
Front cover recipes: Artichokes with Lemon, Ratatouille (see page 85)
Back cover recipes: Veal with Olives and Prosciutto (see page 47) and Tomato and
Roasted Capsicum Soup (see page 79).

Printed by Griffin Press, Adelaide
Printed in Australia
5 4 3 2 1
97 96 95 94 93

CONTENTS

Hearty fare

Casseroles, stews, hotpots and soups are versatile, delicious, economical and nutritious meals to serve for any occasion ranging from family meals to special dinner parties. They are easy to make and can be prepared well in advance, meaning there is little or no last-minute preparation, other than reheating.

These 'moist heat' methods of cooking came into being when someone, somewhere in history, discovered that they could protect meat from the direct heat of a fire by placing it in a clay pot. It then evolved that liquid, vegetables and flavourings were added to the pot and it was learnt that the longer, slower cooking of meat made it more tender, no matter which part of the animal it came from.

Nothing has really changed today — although clay pots aren't often used! Every household has at least one casserole dish or at least some sort of oven-to-table dish or large saucepan. The array of recipes available for this type of cooking seems endless and this book contains some of the best, with lots of hints and tips to help make preparation and cooking even easier.

We tend to lump casseroles, stews and hotpots together, using the terms interchangeably. However, there are differences.

Casseroles are cooked in the oven rather than on top of the stove. Heat circulates around the pot, ensuring even cooking. The meat is cubed and cooked in liquid, e.g. stock. Better cuts of meat are normally used — round, topside or blade steak, or chops — and consequently require shorter cooking times than other methods featured in this book.

Traditionally, a casserole is served from the dish it is cooked in. The most convenient type of casserole dish is one that is flameproof as well, enabling you to brown meat on top of the stove before adding the remaining ingredients and placing the dish in the oven. It also means, if you make the casserole in advance, you can reheat it on top of the stove, making it easier to adjust thickening, seasonings or add last-minute ingredients.

Stews generally use the least expensive cuts of meat — chuck steak, oxtail, neck chops, veal knuckles — which are cubed and cooked in liquid, like casseroles. They require a longer, slower, cooking process. The gentle simmering on top of the stove tenderises the meat and brings out flavours and aromas.

Like casseroles, the flavour of stews improves if cooked a day or so ahead, allowing the sauce to continue its tenderising process as it cools.

A white stew is called a fricassee. These old time favourites are simple to prepare. The meat is first blanched in boiling water before it is added to the cooking pot. In brown stews, the meat is well seared before adding stock and other ingredients. Add a little cream or chopped fresh herbs to an everyday stew to add that special touch. Served with rice, noodles or potatoes, they make for a heart-warming meal.

Hotpots are quite different from stews and casseroles. They are cooked in clear stock with no added thickening agent other than the starch in potatoes, beans, lentils, pasta or rice if used. They are often very thin and are served with a spoon so as not to waste any of the delicious, rich stock.

Braising, although not covered specifically in this book, is an often confused term. Like the methods used for casseroles, braising is done in the oven, but the meat is cooked in larger pieces with a minimum of liquid. This means that the meat is actually steamed.

Soups, originally the basic sustenance that brought the family together, can be a meal in themselves. Although most often served in smaller quantities at the beginning of a meal, a hearty soup, served with chunky bread, can still fill the spot on a cold night.

Soups, although part of the foundations of our cooking traditions, are effortlessly simple to prepare. Fresh ingredients, good stock and aromatic flavourings are all it takes to make a delicious pot of steaming soup. They can be made with every type of food — all it takes is a little imagination. Purée it or keep it chunky, the choice is yours.

More than any type of cooking, casseroles, stews, hotpots and soups encourage the cook to experiment with different flavour combinations. The liquid used in these recipes is usually a stock, either beef, chicken, vegetable or fish. Beef, chicken and vegetable stock may be made from cubes or powders, or liquid stock may be purchased. Remember, these ready prepared stocks are highly seasoned, so be careful before adding more. If preferred, water or wine may be used for a delicious but different flavour. Fish stock is best made fresh the day it is required. Of course, you can make your own

stock, but these convenience foods are great for today's busy lifestyle.

Beef stock is easily made by browning a few beef bones in a little oil. Add a stalk or two of celery, a carrot and an onion, a bouquet garni, a few peppercorns and cover with water. Simmer gently for a few hours, skimming off sediment.

For chicken stock, omit the browning and substitute a chicken carcass or bones for beef bones. If time allows, cool the stock and skim off the fat. Homemade beef and chicken stock freeze well in airtight containers.

Many recipes in this book contain a bouquet garni. Make your own by tying fresh sprigs of herbs, celery studded with peppercorns and a bay leaf together with string. If unavailable, use dried commercial bouquet garni mixtures available in muslin bags.

Whatever method of cooking you choose, *Casseroles, Stews, Hotpots and Hearty Soups* is sure to please. With food costing more every day and homemakers out to work, economical and time-saving meals are a must.

Casseroles, Stews, Hotpots and Hearty Soups provides inexpensive meal alternatives. The recipes can be made in advance and frozen or left to simmer slowly on top of the stove or in the oven while the cook gets on with other chores. Food costs are kept down as meat is stretched by using more vegetables, pulses, pasta and rice. They are also perfect for entertaining. Using a little imagination, something everyday can be transformed into

something extra special, giving you more time to be with your guests.

The recipes in this book cover ideas for beef, lamb, pork, veal, poultry and game, fish and vegetables. In each chapter an old favourite has been modified to give you a healthier version for today's more health conscious lifestyle. Use

these ideas to modify other recipes in the book if you are watching cholesterol or kilojoule levels.

Casseroles, Stews, Hotpots and Hearty Soups will become invaluable in your kitchen.

Beef

*B*eef is a basic ingredient for such famous casseroles as beef in red wine. The use of beef stock, red wine, vegetables and the imaginative use of herbs and spices, make some of the most delicious and wonderfully aromatic of meals.

SAUSAGE AND TOMATO SOUP

- 1½ cups (280 g/9 oz) lentils
- 6 to 8 cups (1½ to 2 litres/48 fl oz to 70 fl oz) boiling water
- 2 tablespoons olive oil
- 500 g (1 lb) beef sausages (or Kransky, colbassi or Polish sausage), sliced
- 250 g (8 oz) ham, chopped
- 1 onion, chopped
- 1 green capsicum (pepper), seeded and chopped
- 1 carrot, chopped
- 1 clove garlic, crushed
- 8 cups (2 litres/70 fl oz) beef stock
- 425 g (13½ oz) canned tomatoes, chopped
- 1 bay leaf
- ½ teaspoon each ground cumin and oregano
- seasonings, to taste
- 4 spinach leaves, shredded

Place lentils and water in a large saucepan. Boil for 3 minutes. Drain well. Set aside.

Heat oil in a large saucepan. Cook sausages for 5 minutes. Add ham, onion, capsicum, carrot and garlic. Cook gently, stirring occasionally, for 10 minutes.

Blend in stock, tomatoes, lentils and seasonings. Bring to the boil. Reduce heat. Simmer for 45 minutes or until lentils are tender. Stir in spinach. Simmer for a further 5 minutes.

SERVES 6 TO 8

Picture previous pages: Italian-style Beef (page 14), Hearty Beef and Vegetable Soup (page 9)

SPICY BEEF AND BEAN SOUP

- 2 tablespoons olive oil
- 2 onions, chopped
- 2 cloves garlic, crushed
- 1 green capsicum (pepper), seeded and chopped
- 750 g (1½ lb) chuck steak, trimmed and cubed
- 8 cups (2 litres/70 fl oz) beef stock
- 2½ cups (500 g/1 lb) dried red kidney beans, soaked in water overnight and drained
- 425 g (13½ oz) canned tomato purée
- 2 teaspoons chilli powder
- 1 teaspoon chilli sauce
- 1 teaspoon ground cumin
- seasonings, to taste

Heat oil in a large saucepan. Sauté onions and garlic until onions are tender. Add capsicum. Sauté for 2 minutes.

Blend in all remaining ingredients. Bring to the boil. Reduce heat. Simmer, covered, for 2 hours or until beans and meat are tender. Serve with rolls.

SERVES 6 TO 8

BEEF AND PEA SOUP

- 1 cup (185 g/6 oz) dried chickpeas
- 3 cups (750 ml/25 fl oz) water
- 2 tablespoons oil
- 250 g (8 oz) gravy beef, trimmed and cubed
- 2 onions, chopped
- 2 cabbage leaves, shredded
- 2 sticks celery, sliced
- 1 zucchini (courgette), sliced
- 1 leek, sliced
- 8 cups (2 litres/70 fl oz) beef stock
- 4 bacon bones
- 2 bay leaves
- 1 teaspoon dried thyme
- 1 cup (155 g/5 oz) macaroni
- seasonings, to taste
- grated Parmesan cheese

Place chickpeas in a saucepan with water. Bring to the boil. Simmer for 5 minutes. Remove from heat. Allow to stand for 1 hour.

Heat oil in a frying pan. Brown meat well. Transfer to a large saucepan. Add onions, cabbage, celery, zucchini and leek to frying pan. Sauté for 3 minutes. Set aside.

Add drained chickpeas to meat with stock, bacon bones and herbs. Simmer, covered, for 1½ to 2 hours or until chickpeas are tender.

Stir in onion mixture, macaroni and seasonings. Simmer for a further 15 minutes or until pasta is tender. Remove any meat from bones. Add to soup. Discard bones. Sprinkle with cheese. Serve with crusty bread.

SERVES 6 TO 8

WINTERY SOUP

- 1 tablespoon olive oil
- 1 onion, chopped
- 250 g (8 oz) minced steak
- ½ cabbage, shredded
- 2 leeks, sliced
- 1 tomato, peeled and chopped
- 6 cups (1½ litres/48 fl oz) beef stock
- 1 tablespoon soy sauce
- 2 teaspoons French mustard
- seasonings, to taste
- chopped fresh parsley

CABBAGE

When using shredded cabbage in a recipe ensure that hard veins and core are removed.

Heat oil in a large saucepan. Sauté onion until tender. Add mince. Brown well, breaking up with a spoon as it cooks.

Add cabbage, leeks and tomato. Cook for 2 minutes. Stir in stock, soy, mustard and seasonings.

Bring to the boil. Reduce heat. Simmer for 10 minutes. Sprinkle with parsley. Serve with toasted cheese fingers.

SERVES 4 TO 6

HEARTY BEEF AND VEGETABLE SOUP

2 tablespoons olive oil
1 kg (2 lb) beef bones
1 onion, chopped
6 cups (1½ litres/48 fl oz) beef stock

3 carrots, chopped
3 sticks celery, sliced
2 zucchini (courgettes), sliced
1 turnip, chopped
1 leek, sliced
1 potato, chopped
½ cup (90 g/3 oz) barley
3 peppercorns
3 cloves
2 bay leaves
½ teaspoon each basil, marjoram and thyme
seasonings, to taste
125 g (4 oz) button mushrooms, halved

Heat oil in a large saucepan. Add bones and onion. Cook, stirring, for 5 minutes.

Add remaining ingredients to pan, except mushrooms. Bring to the boil. Reduce heat. Simmer for 40 to 45 minutes.

Remove any meat from bones. Add to soup. Discard bones. Stir in mushrooms. Simmer for a further 10 minutes. Serve with crusty bread.

SERVES 4 TO 6

ONIONS

Onions should be peeled for every recipe, unless otherwise stated. Peel using a sharp knife. If the onion is cold, you may cry less while chopping it.

Hearty Beef and Vegetable Soup

CIDER HOTPOT

90 g (3 oz) butter or margarine

750 g (1½ lb) topside steak, sliced thinly

2 carrots, sliced

2 turnips, peeled and chopped

1 onion, sliced

3 tablespoons plain (all-purpose) flour

2 cups (500 ml/16 fl oz) apple cider

1 beef stock cube, crumbled

seasonings, to taste

500 g (1 lb) potatoes, peeled and sliced

¾ cup (90 g/3 oz) grated cheese

Preheat oven to 180°C (350°F).

Melt butter in a large frying pan. Add meat. Brown well. Remove from pan. Add carrots, turnips and onion to pan. Fry gently for 10 minutes. Stir in flour. Cook for 1 minute.

Remove pan from heat. Gradually blend in cider. Return to heat. Cook, stirring constantly, until sauce boils and thickens.

Stir in meat, stock cube and seasonings. Simmer for 5 minutes. Transfer beef and vegetable mixture to a large ovenproof dish. Arrange potato slices on top. Bake, covered, for 1½ to 2 hours.

Sprinkle with cheese. Bake for a further 15 minutes or until cheese melts and is golden.

SERVES 4

PEELING TOMATOES

Peel tomatoes by piercing the skin in a few places. Cover with boiling water. Leave for 1 minute. Drain well. The skin will peel away easily.

Beef and Cider Hotpot

BOUQUET GARNI

Prepare a bouquet garni by tying together a sprig of parsley, a bay leaf and a piece of celery studded with peppercorns. Other herbs may also be used. Alternatively, commercially prepared bouquet garnis are available from your supermarket.

BEEF GOULASH

2 tablespoons oil

3 onions, thinly sliced

750 g (1½ lb) chuck or blade steak, cubed

2 cloves garlic, crushed

1 tablespoon paprika

pinch each cumin and marjoram

3 tomatoes, peeled and chopped

1 green capsicum (pepper) seeded and chopped

2½ cups (625 ml/1 pt) water

½ cup (125 ml/4 fl oz) dry red wine

2 beef stock cubes, crumbled

3 tablespoons cornflour (cornstarch)

¼ cup (60 ml/2 fl oz) water

seasonings, to taste

¼ cup (60 ml/2 fl oz) sour cream

Heat oil in a large, heavy-based pan. Fry onions until golden brown. Add meat. Cook gently for about 8 minutes, stirring occasionally.

Stir in garlic, paprika, cumin and marjoram. Cook for 1 minute more.

Add tomatoes, green capsicum, water, wine and stock cubes. Simmer, covered, for 1½ hours or until meat is tender.

Blend cornflour with water. Stir into goulash. Simmer, stirring constantly, for 3 minutes. Season to taste. Top goulash with a dollop of sour cream before serving. Serve with boiled potatoes, noodles or rice.

SERVES 4

BEEF TOMATO CASSEROLE

2 tablespoons oil

1kg (2 lb) chuck steak, cubed

4 rashers (125 g/4 oz) rindless bacon, chopped

4 onions, sliced

2 cloves garlic, crushed

3 tablespoons plain (all-purpose) flour

1½ tablespoons tomato paste

1 beef stock cube, crumbled

1¼ cups (315 ml/10 fl oz) dry red wine

1¼ cups (315 ml/10 fl oz) water

6 tomatoes, peeled and chopped

1 bouquet garni

seasonings, to taste

6 black olives

1 tablespoon chopped fresh parsley

Heat oil in a large, heavy-based pan. Add beef and bacon. Cook, stirring occasionally, until well browned.

Stir in onions and garlic. Sauté for 1 minute. Sprinkle over flour. Cook, stirring, for 1 minute. Blend in tomato paste and stock cube. Remove from heat.

Mix in wine, water, tomatoes, bouquet garni and seasonings. Simmer, covered, for 1½ to 2 hours or until meat is tender. Just before serving, stir in olives and parsley. Serve with rice and vegetables.

This mixture may be transferred to a casserole dish and baked, covered, in a moderate oven (180°C/350°F) for the same amount of time.

SERVES 4 TO 6

COUNTRY COBBLER

2 tablespoons oil

750 g (1½ lb) chuck or round
    steak, cubed

1 onion, chopped

1 carrot, chopped

6 tablespoons plain (all purpose)
    flour

2 tablespoons tomato paste

1 beef stock cube, crumbled

1¼ cups (315 ml/10 fl oz) beer

1¼ cups (315 ml/10 fl oz) water

1 clove garlic, crushed

pinch ground rosemary

seasonings, to taste

1 tablespoon chopped fresh parsley

TOPPING

1½ cups (180 g/6 oz) self-raising
    flour, sifted

pinch salt (optional)

60 g (2 oz) butter or margarine,
    cubed

2 stalks celery, chopped

2 tablespoons chopped fresh
    parsley

½ cup (125 ml/4 fl oz) milk

1 tablespoon milk, extra

Preheat oven to 180°C (350°F).

Heat oil in a large frying pan. Brown meat well. Add onion and carrot. Cook, stirring, for 2 to 3 minutes. Stir in flour. Cook, stirring, for 1 minute. Blend in tomato paste and stock cube. Remove from heat.

Blend in beer, water, garlic, rosemary and seasonings. Return to heat. Simmer for 3 minutes. Transfer to a casserole dish.

Bake, covered, for 1½ hours or until meat is tender.

To Prepare Topping: Mix flour and salt together in a bowl. Rub in the butter using fingertips, until mixture resembles fine breadcrumbs. Stir in celery and parsley.

Add milk all at once. Mix lightly to form a soft dough. Turn onto a floured board. Knead lightly.

Roll dough out until 2 cm (¾ in) thick. Cut out as many circles as possible using a floured 7 cm (2¾ in) cutter. Then, using a 1 cm (½ in) cutter, cut a hole in the centre of each dough circle.

Overlap circles on top of casserole. Brush with extra milk. Bake for 20 minutes or until the topping is golden. Serve sprinkled with parsley.

SERVES 4

AROMATIC BEEF
MARINADE

8 carrots, thinly sliced

1 onion, finely chopped

3 sprigs parsley

1 bay leaf

½ teaspoon dried thyme

seasonings, to taste

Country Cobbler

1½ kg (3 lb) piece round steak

1½ cups (375 ml/12 fl oz) red wine

2 tablespoons olive oil

3 extra onions, finely chopped

4 cloves garlic, crushed

12 large mushrooms, chopped

1 teaspoon fresh lemon juice

8 rashers (250 g/8 oz) rindless bacon, chopped

3 tablespoons plain (all purpose) flour

½ cup (125 ml/4 fl oz) beef stock

Place carrots, onion, parsley, bay leaf, thyme and seasonings in a bowl. Add beef and wine. Cover and marinate in the refrigerator for 24 hours, turning meat every 8 hours.

Transfer meat to a plate. Pat dry with paper towels. Strain and reserve the marinade.

Preheat oven to 180°C (350°F).

Heat oil in a large frying pan. Brown meat on all sides over a high heat. Transfer to a plate. Sauté extra onions and garlic in same oil for 3 minutes. Add mushrooms and lemon juice. Continue cooking for 5 minutes.

In another pan, fry bacon until crisp. Set aside. Blend flour into onion and mushroom mixture. Remove from heat.

Gradually blend combined stock and reserved marinade into onion and mushroom mixture. Return to heat. Add bacon. Bring to the boil, stirring.

Place beef in a casserole dish. Pour over onion and mushroom mixture. Bake, covered, for 2½ hours. Serve with new potatoes and vegetables of choice.

SERVES 8

MEXICAN HOTPOT

For a more authentic South American flavour, increase the amount of chilli powder used and add 315 g (10 oz) corn kernels, drained. Serve with a dollop of sour cream and chopped avocado if liked.

2 tablespoons oil

1 large onion, chopped

1 green capsicum (pepper), seeded and chopped

500 g (1 lb) minced steak

3 tablespoons plain (all purpose) flour

pinch each paprika and chilli powder

2 tablespoons tomato paste

1 beef stock cube, crumbled

1¾ cups (440 ml/14 fl oz) water

1 bouquet garni

315 g (10 oz) canned red kidney beans, drained

seasonings, to taste

Heat oil in a large saucepan. Sauté onion until tender. Add green capsicum. Cook 1 minute. Add mince to pan. Cook until well browned, breaking up with a spoon as it cooks.

Stir in flour, paprika and chilli. Cook, stirring, for 1 minute. Mix in tomato paste and stock cube. Remove from heat.

Gradually blend in water. Return to heat. Cook, stirring constantly, until mixture boils. Add the bouquet garni. Simmer for 30 minutes.

Stir in kidney beans and seasonings. Cook for a further 5 minutes. Serve with boiled rice.

SERVES 4

CLASSIC BEEF AND OLIVE CASSEROLE

30 g (1 oz) butter or margarine

1 tablespoon oil

1kg (2 lb) chuck or topside steak, trimmed and cut into large cubes

4 carrots, sliced

2 onions, quartered

2 stalks celery, sliced

1 clove garlic, crushed

3 tablespoons plain (all-purpose) flour

425 g (13½ oz) canned tomatoes

1¼ cups (315 ml/10 fl oz) water

½ cup (125 ml/4 fl oz) sherry

1 beef stock cube, crumbled

1 bay leaf

few sprigs parsley

seasonings, to taste

6 stuffed green olives, sliced

Preheat oven to 180°C (350°F).

Heat butter and oil in a large frying pan. Sauté meat pieces until well browned. Transfer to a casserole dish.

Add carrots, onions, celery and garlic to same pan. Fry over a low heat for about 5 minutes.

Stir in flour. Cook for 1 minute. Gradually stir in tomatoes, water, sherry, stock cube and seasonings. Cook, stirring constantly, until mixture boils and thickens. Pour over meat in casserole.

Bake, covered, for 2 to 2½ hours or until meat is tender. Remove bay leaf and parsley. Stir in olives. Serve with boiled potatoes and green beans.

SERVE 4 TO 6

RUSSIAN BEEF CASSEROLE WITH CARAWAY RICE

- 2 tablespoons oil
- 1 kg (1 lb) chuck or blade steak, trimmed and cubed
- 3 stalks celery, sliced
- 1 large onion, chopped
- 450 g (14½ oz) canned pineapple pieces
- ⅔ cup (150 ml/5 fl oz) water
- 1 tablespoon tomato paste
- 1 tablespoon chopped fresh parsley
- 1 beef stock cube, crumbled
- ½ teaspoon Worcestershire sauce
- ¼ teaspoon sugar
- seasonings, to taste

CARAWAY RICE

- 1½ cups (235 g/7½ oz) long-grain rice
- 30 g/1 oz butter
- 2 teaspoons caraway seeds

Preheat oven to 180°C (350°F).

Heat oil in a large frying pan. Add meat. Brown well on all sides. Transfer to a casserole dish. Add celery and onion to same pan. Sauté for 3 minutes or until onion is tender. Add to casserole.

Drain pineapple, reserving liquid. Combine pineapple juice with all remaining ingredients except pineapple pieces. Pour over meat.

Bake, covered, for 1½ hours or until meat is tender. More stock may be added if required.

Fifteen minutes before the end of cooking time, stir through pineapple pieces. Serve with Caraway Rice.

To Prepare Caraway Rice: Cook rice in a large saucepan of salted boiling water. Boil for 12 minutes or until tender. Drain well. Return to pan. Stir in butter and caraway seeds.

SERVES 4 TO 6

Russian Beef Casserole with Caraway Rice

ITALIAN-STYLE BEEF

- 1 tablespoon olive oil
- 1 onion, sliced
- 1 clove garlic, crushed
- 500 g (1 lb) minced beef
- 425 g (13½ oz) canned tomatoes
- 1 cup (155 g/5 oz) shell pasta, cooked
- ½ cup (125 ml/4 fl oz) red wine
- 2 tablespoons tomato paste
- 1 tablespoon chopped fresh basil
- 2 teaspoons brown sugar
- 1 teaspoon paprika
- ½ teaspoon dried oregano
- 1 cup (125 g/4 oz) grated tasty cheese

Preheat oven to 180°C (350°F).

Heat oil in a large frying pan. Sauté onion and garlic until onion is tender. Add mince. Brown well, breaking up with a spoon as it cooks.

Mix in all remaining ingredients, except cheese. Bring to the boil. Reduce heat. Simmer for 10 minutes. Transfer mixture to a casserole dish.

Sprinkle with cheese. Bake for 20 to 25 minutes, or until cheese melts and is brown. Serve with salad and toasted foccacia bread.

SERVES 4 TO 6

Italian-style Beef

HERBED BEEF STEW

1kg (2 lb) lean stewing steak
(eg blade), trimmed and cubed

6 rashers (180 g/6 oz) rindless
bacon, diced

1½ cups (375 ml/12 oz) red wine

90 g (3 oz) butter or margarine

250 g (8 oz) carrots, sliced

2 leeks, sliced

1 clove garlic, crushed

2 tomatoes, peeled and chopped

seasonings, to taste

1 bouquet garni

2 cups (500 ml/16 fl oz) beef stock

3 tablespoons oil

155 g (5 oz) pickling onions,
peeled

185 g (6 oz) button mushrooms

1 tablespoon chopped fresh parsley

Place steak and bacon in a bowl with wine. Marinate for several hours or overnight, stirring occasionally.

Preheat oven to 150°C (300°F).

Remove meat from marinade, reserving liquid. Pat meat dry. Melt half the butter in a frying pan. Fry meat until evenly browned. Transfer to a casserole dish.

Melt remaining butter in the same pan. Sauté carrots, leeks and garlic for 5 minutes. Stir in tomatoes and

Herbed Beef Stew

seasonings. Pour over meat with the reserved marinade and bouquet garni.

Pour stock into frying pan. Bring to the boil, stirring well to loosen sediment. Add to casserole. Bake, covered, for 2 to 2¼ hours.

Heat oil in a frying pan. Sauté onions and mushrooms for 3 minutes. Stir into casserole with parsley. Bake for a further 45 minutes. Remove the bouquet garni before serving with creamed potatoes.

SERVES 4 TO 6

OXTAIL STEW

If possible, after baking, cool and refrigerate overnight so that the fat rises to the surface and sets. Remove fat, then reheat for about 1 hour.

> 1kg (2 lb) oxtail, cut into pieces
> ½ cup (60 g/2 oz) plain (all-purpose) flour
> 3 tablespoons oil
> 3 stalks celery, thinly sliced
> 2 turnips, cut into chunks
> 2 large carrots, cut into pieces lengthways
> 1 large onion, sliced
> 4 cups (1 litre/32 fl oz) boiling water
> 3 beef stock cubes, crumbled
> 2 tablespoons tomato paste
> 1 bay leaf
> 1 bouquet garni
> ½ teaspoon ground oregano
> seasonings, to taste
> 1 tablespoon chopped fresh parsley

Preheat oven to 160°C (325°F).

Remove excess fat from oxtail. Toss in flour. Heat oil in a large frying pan. Brown meat well. Drain on paper towel. Place in a large casserole dish.

Sauté celery, turnips, carrots and onion in same pan until onion is tender. Drain well. Transfer to the casserole dish.

Combine water, stock cubes and tomato paste. Pour into casserole dish with bay leaf, bouquet garni, oregano and seasonings.

Bake, covered, for 3 hours. Sprinkle with parsley. Serve with new potatoes and vegetables in season.

SERVES 4 TO 6

Oxtail Stew

PEPPERY BEEF HOTPOT

If using marrow bones, remove the marrow and spread on toasted French bread as an accompaniment. Discard the bones.

- *1½ kg (3 lb) piece round or chuck steak*
- *2 marrow bones (optional)*
- *10 peppercorns*
- *1 tablespoon chopped fresh parsley*
- *1 bay leaf*
- *½ teaspoon dried thyme*
- *salt, to taste*
- *water*
- *2 onions*
- *4 cloves*
- *250 g (8 oz) potatoes, cubed*
- *250 g (8 oz) carrots, sliced*
- *250 g (8 oz) turnips, cubed*
- *2 leeks, sliced*
- *2 stalks celery, sliced*
- *1 small cabbage, roughly chopped*
- *½ cup (125 ml/4 fl oz) red wine*

Tie meat securely to maintain shape. Place the beef, marrow bones, peppercorns, parsley, bay leaf, thyme and salt in a large, heavy pan. Almost cover with water.

Bring water to boil. Reduce heat. Simmer, partially covered, for 2 to 2½ hours, skimming off sediment as it rises.

Spike one of the onions with cloves. Slice the other. Add these to the pot with the potatoes, carrots, turnips, leeks and celery. Simmer, partially covered, for 1 hour.

Stir in cabbage. Simmer for 30 minutes. Remove the meat and vegetables to a serving platter. Keep warm.

Skim any fat and sediment from stock. Add the wine. Bring to the boil. Serve the sliced meat and vegetables with the stock, French bread, pickles, mustard and sea salt.

SERVES 4 TO 6

PREPARING LEEKS

Clean leeks well as the layers are often filled with dirt. Do this by trimming and slicing down the centre lengthways. Wash between the layers. Use as directed.

CRUSTY CASSEROLE

- *2 tablespoons oil*
- *750 g (1½ lb) chuck steak, cubed*
- *2 onions, sliced*
- *1 tablespoon plain (all-purpose) flour*
- *2 cups (500 ml/16 fl oz) hot water*
- *1¼ cups (315 ml/10 fl oz) beer*
- *1 clove garlic, crushed*
- *1 bouquet garni*
- *1 teaspoon vinegar*
- *pinch each sugar and nutmeg*
- *seasonings, to taste*
- *6 slices French bread*
- *2 tablespoons Dijon mustard*

Preheat oven to 180°C (350°F).

Heat oil in a large frying pan. Sauté meat until well browned. Add onions. Sauté until golden. Stir in flour. Blend in water, beer, garlic, bouquet garni, vinegar, sugar, nutmeg and seasonings. Bring to the boil, stirring constantly. Transfer to a casserole dish.

Bake, covered, for 2 hours. Skim the surface to remove sediment. Remove bouquet garni. Spread each slice of bread with mustard.

Arrange bread slices over top of the casserole, pushing each slice below the surface so that it becomes soaked with gravy.

Return casserole to the oven. Bake, uncovered, for 40 minutes or until the top is crusty and golden. Serve with vegetables or salad.

SERVES 4

FRESH BREADCRUMBS

Make fresh breadcrumbs by placing cubes of crustless, day old bread in a food processor or blender. Process until well chopped. Use immediately or freeze in plastic bags for later use. Defrost before using.

SERVING IDEAS

Toss some finely chopped fresh parsley or other herb through cooked rice or pasta for a flavoursome and attractive accompaniment.

SLICING MEAT

Meat is easier to cut and slice while still partially frozen.

LIQUID STOCK

A good quality liquid stock is available in cartons from supermarkets.

CHUCK STEAK

This can be bought with the bone in, or boneless and is commonly used for roasting, braising and stewing. It is leaner than some other cuts of beef and a good source of protein and other nutrients.

HUNGARIAN MEATBALLS

- 500 g (1 lb) minced steak
- ½ cup (60 g/2 oz) fresh breadcrumbs
- 1 egg, lightly beaten
- 1 tablespoon chopped fresh parsley
- seasonings, to taste
- 2 tablespoons plain (all-purpose) flour
- 2 tablespoons oil
- 3 large onions, sliced
- 3 tablespoons tomato paste
- 1 tablespoon paprika
- 2 tablespoons plain (all-purpose) flour, extra
- 1¼ cups (315 ml/10 fl oz) water
- 1 beef stock cube, crumbled, and dissolved in a little hot water
- ¼ teaspoon caraway seeds (optional)
- 500 g (1 lb) potatoes, peeled and thinly sliced

Preheat oven to 180°C (350°F).

Combine mince, breadcrumbs, egg, parsley and seasonings in a bowl. Shape into about 12 even-sized meatballs. Dust lightly with flour. Heat oil in a large frying pan. Add meatballs. Brown well all over. Transfer to a casserole dish.

Add a little more oil to pan if required. Sauté onions until golden. Blend in tomato paste and paprika. Cook for 1 minute. Stir in extra flour. Cook, stirring, for 1 minute. Remove from heat.

Gradually blend in combined water and stock cube. Return pan to heat. Bring to the boil, stirring constantly. Stir in caraway seeds. Pour sauce over meatballs.

Arrange potatoes around top of dish. Bake for about 45 minutes. Serve with salad and crusty bread.

SERVES 4

Beef Makeover

To modify this recipe to a healthier version, reducing fat, kilojoules and cholesterol:

Meat is trimmed of all fat and the amount of meat used is halved. The quantity of mushrooms is doubled to compensate.

Olive oil is used in place of cooking oil.

A small amount of polyunsaturated margarine is used in place of butter.

Ham, with all fat removed, is used in place of bacon.

No salt or sugar are used.

No stock cubes are used, reducing salt.

BEEF IN RED WINE

- 2 tablespoons olive oil
- 750 g (1½ lb) topside or round steak, trimmed and cubed
- 500 g (1 lb) mushrooms, thickly sliced
- 125 g (4 oz) ham, sliced
- 60 g (2 oz) polyunsaturated margarine
- 1 clove garlic, crushed
- 2½ tablespoons plain (all-purpose) flour
- 1½ cups (375 ml/12 fl oz) red wine
- 1½ cups (375 ml/12 fl oz) water
- seasonings, to taste
- 12 pickling onions
- 1 bay leaf

Preheat oven to 180°C (350°F).

Heat oil in a large frying pan. Brown meat well on all sides.

Drain on crumpled kitchen paper. Transfer to a casserole dish.

Sauté mushrooms and ham in same pan for 1 minute. Transfer to a plate. Set aside. Melt margarine in same pan. Sauté garlic for 1 minute. Add flour. Cook, stirring, until lightly browned. Remove from heat.

Gradually blend in wine, water and seasonings. Return to heat. Cook, stirring constantly, until sauce boils and thickens.

Add onions and bay leaf to casserole dish. Pour over sauce. Bake, covered, for 1 hour.

Remove casserole from oven. Stir in mushroom mixture. Bake, covered, for a further 30 minutes. Serve with boiled new potatoes and vegetables in season.

SERVES 4 TO 6

Lamb

*L*amb is much more delicately flavoured than beef, and goes beautifully with vegetables, stock, herbs and spices. It is also more tender than mutton, which used to be used, so casseroles and similar dishes cooked with lamb have shorter cooking times than before.

The best lamb is available in spring and the colour for young lamb should be light pink; older lamb light red.

Green serving ware from Home & Garden on the Mall, Skygarden, Sydney
Rug and wine basket from Made n' Earth, Mid City Centre, Sydney

SCOTCH BROTH

2 tablespoons olive oil

2 lamb shanks

1 onion, chopped

2 carrots, chopped

2 stalks celery, chopped

1 turnip, diced

8 cups (2 litres/70 fl oz) beef stock or water

½ cup (90 g/3 oz) barley

⅓ cup (60 g/2 oz) split peas

2 bay leaves

½ teaspoon dried thyme

seasonings, to taste

Heat oil in a large saucepan. Add shanks and onion. Cook, until well browned.

Stir in vegetables. Cook gently, stirring, for 5 minutes.

Add all remaining ingredients. Bring to the boil. Reduce heat. Simmer for 1 hour or until vegetables, barley and peas are tender.

Remove meat from shanks. Return to soup. Discard bones. Serve with crusty bread or homemade scones.

SERVES 4 TO 6

Picture previous pages: Creamy Curried Lamb (page 30), Country-style Vegetable Soup (page 24)

LAMB COOKED WITH RICE AND VEGETABLES

2 tablespoons oil

30 g (1 oz) butter or margarine

2 onions, chopped

2 leeks, sliced

2 carrots, sliced

1 stalk celery, chopped

6 chump chops

3 tablespoons plain (all-purpose) flour, seasoned

1 bay leaf

sprig of fresh thyme or ½ teaspoon dried

pinch nutmeg

seasonings, to taste

2 cups (500 ml/16 fl oz) water

1 chicken stock cube, crumbled

1½ cups (235 g/7½ oz) rice

1 cup (125 g/4 oz) frozen peas

Preheat oven to 180°C (350°F).

Heat oil and butter together in a flameproof casserole dish. Sauté onions, leeks, carrots and celery until tender. Transfer to a plate.

Dust chops in flour. Fry in same oil until well browned on both sides. Return vegetables to dish with bay leaf, thyme, nutmeg and seasonings. Cook 1 minute.

Blend in water and stock cubes. Bring to the boil. Bake for 40 minutes or until meat is tender.

Add rice to dish. Bring to the boil on top of the stove. Stir in peas. Bake, covered, for a further 20 minutes or until rice is tender. Add extra stock during cooking if the rice absorbs too much liquid. Serve with vegetables of choice.

SERVES 4 TO 6

LAMB, EGGPLANT AND BEAN CASSEROLE

If using dried haricot beans, soak them overnight beforehand.

2 large eggplants (aubergines), cut into 1½ cm (¾ in) thick slices

salt

4 lamb forequarter chops or 4 middle lamb cutlets

3 tablespoons plain (all-purpose flour)

1 tablespoon curry powder

1 tablespoon oil

2 onions, sliced

4 carrots, sliced

2 sticks celery, sliced

125 g (4 oz) haricot beans

3 cups (750 ml/24 fl oz) beef stock

1 tablespoon tomato paste

Sprinkle eggplant slices with salt, leave for 30 minutes, rinse and drain.

Preheat oven to 180°C (350°F).

Trim any excess fat from the chops. Mix flour and curry powder together, then toss lamb in it. Shake off any excess.

Heat oil in frypan and brown lamb well on both sides. Drain, and transfer meat to casserole dish. Gently sauté onions, carrots and celery in frypan for 5 minutes, then add to casserole.

Boil beans for 10 minutes in salted water. Remove the scum from the surface, drain and add to casserole with eggplants.

Add tomato paste to stock and pour over meat and vegetables. Cover casserole and bake for 1 to 1½ hours or until meat and beans are tender. Adjust seasoning to taste before serving.

SERVES 4

Lamb, Eggplant and Bean Casserole

COUNTRY-STYLE VEGETABLE SOUP

2 tablespoons oil

500 g (1 lb) lean lamb, cubed

1 onion, chopped

2 tablespoons tomato paste

8 cups (2 litres/70 fl oz) beef stock or water

4 carrots, sliced

2 potatoes, chopped

2 stalks celery, sliced

1 leek, sliced

1 cup (125 g/4 oz) green beans, sliced

½ cabbage, shredded

¼ cauliflower, cut into florets

2 spinach leaves, shredded

seasonings, to taste

chopped fresh parsley

Heat oil in a large saucepan. Brown meat and onion well. Stir in tomato paste. Cook 1 minute.

Blend in stock, carrots, potatoes, celery and leek. Bring to the boil. Reduce heat. Simmer for 1 hour or until meat is tender.

Stir in beans, cabbage and cauliflower. Simmer for a further 20 minutes. Blend in spinach and seasonings. Simmer for 5 minutes. Sprinkle with parsley. Serve with crusty bread.

SERVES 4 TO 6

Country-style Vegetable Soup

IRISH HOTPOT

1kg (2 lb) boned leg of lamb, cubed

3¾ cups (940 ml/31 fl oz) water

seasonings, to taste

1kg (2 lb) potatoes, sliced

500 g (1 lb) onions, sliced

2 leeks, sliced

1 tablespoon chopped fresh parsley

Preheat oven to 180°C (350°F).

Place meat in a saucepan with water and seasonings. Bring to the boil. Skim off any scum that rises to the surface.

Transfer mixture to a large casserole dish with half the potatoes and all of the onions and leeks.

Bake, covered, for 1½ hours. Add the remaining potatoes. Bake for a further 30 minutes, adding more water if required. Sprinkle with parsley. Serve with salad and crusty bread or vegetables of choice.

SERVES 4 TO 6

LAMB WITH CIDER

1 tablespoon oil

1 kg (2 lb) boned leg of lamb, cubed

1 onion, chopped

1 tablespoon tomato paste

3 cups (750 ml/25 fl oz) water

1¼ cups (315 ml/10 fl oz) cider

1 beef stock cube, crumbled

seasonings, to taste

2 tablespoons plain (all-purpose) flour

Heat oil in a large pan. Add meat. Brown well on all sides. Transfer to a plate.

Sauté onion in same oil until tender. Stir in tomato paste. Cook for 1 minute. Blend in water, cider, stock cube and seasonings. Bring to the boil. Reduce heat. Stir in meat. Simmer for 1½ hours or until meat is tender.

Blend flour with a little of the stew gravy until smooth. Gradually blend into casserole, stirring constantly, until mixture boils and thickens. Simmer for 3 minutes. Serve casserole with boiled baby onions, peas, carrots and turnips.

SERVES 4 TO 6

HEALTHY VEGETABLES

Retain skin on vegetables such as potatoes, carrots, turnips, to increase the fibre content of the dish.

SPICED LASAGNE

2 tablespoons oil

1 onion, finely chopped

550 g (1 lb) lamb, minced

1 teaspoon chilli powder

1 green capsicum (pepper), seeded and chopped

1 tablespoon tomato paste

salt and freshly ground black pepper

1¾ cups (420 ml/14 fl oz) beef stock

2 tablespoons raisins

185 g (6 oz) lasagne sheets

1 cup (250 ml/8 fl oz) natural yoghurt

1 egg

1 tablespoon chopped walnuts

1 red capsicum (pepper), seeded and cut into rings

Heat oil in a frypan and sauté onion until softened. Add lamb and stir to brown it evenly. Stir in chilli powder, adding more if desired. Cook for 1 minute. Add green capsicum, tomato paste, seasoning to taste, beef stock and raisins. Bring to the boil, cover, and simmer for 40 minutes.

Preheat oven to 180°C (350°F).

Cook lasagne sheets in boiling salted water for about 5 minutes or until just tender. Wash the lasagne briskly under cold running water to remove the starch and separate the sheets. Drain and dry sheets on a clean cloth or paper towel.

Spoon a layer of meat into the bottom of an ovenproof dish. Cover with a layer of lasagne. Repeat until sauce and lasagne are all used, finishing with a layer of sauce on top.

Beat together yoghurt, egg and walnuts. Pour over the top of the casserole. Arrange red capsicum over the yoghurt. Bake for 20 minutes.

SERVES 6

GARLIC POT ROAST LAMB

2 kg (4 lb) leg of lamb, boned, trimmed, rolled and tied

seasonings, to taste

2 cloves garlic, slivered

30 g (1 oz) butter or margarine

1 tablespoon oil

4 carrots, cut into large pieces

4 parsnips, cut into large pieces

4 onions, quartered

2 cups (500 ml/16 fl oz) beef stock

2 cups (185 g/6 oz) cooked lima beans

1 tablespoon cornflour (cornstarch)

Sprinkle lamb with seasonings. Lightly cut the skin in several places. Insert garlic slivers.

Heat butter and oil in a large flameproof dish. Brown lamb well on all sides. Transfer to a plate. Lightly brown carrots, parsnips and onions in the same oil. Transfer to a plate.

Pour fat from casserole dish. Return lamb with stock. Bring to the boil. Simmer, partially covered, for 1½ hours.

Add vegetables to pan. Simmer for a further 30 minutes or until meat and vegetables are tender.

Stir lima beans into pan. Simmer for a few minutes or until lima beans are heated through. Remove meat and vegetables to serving plates. Keep warm.

Skim any fat from liquid remaining in casserole. Blend cornflour with a little of the liquid to form a smooth paste. Blend into casserole. Cook, stirring constantly, until sauce boils and thickens. Simmer for 3 minutes. Strain. Serve meat sliced with vegetables and sauce.

SERVES 4 TO 6

ALMOND LAMB CURRY

2 tablespoons oil

2 onions, sliced

1kg (2 lb) boned shoulder lamb, cubed

2 tablespoons curry powder

1 tablespoon ground turmeric

1 teaspoon ground ginger

155 ml (5 fl oz) beef stock

2 tablespoons mango chutney

2 tablespoons raisins

1 tablespoon tomato paste

seasonings, to taste

½ cup (125 ml/4 fl oz) sour cream or natural yoghurt

2 tablespoons slivered almonds

Heat oil in a large, heavy-based pan. Sauté onions until tender. Add lamb. Brown well. Stir in curry powder, turmeric and ginger. Cook gently for 3 minutes.

Blend in stock, chutney, raisins, tomato paste and seasonings. Bring to the boil, stirring constantly. Reduce heat. Simmer, covered, for 45 minutes or until the meat is tender.

Stir in sour cream and half the almonds. Simmer for a further 10 minutes. Serve curry with rice and sambals (see Note). Garnish with remaining almonds.

SERVES 4 TO 6

SERVING CURRIES

Sambals are side dishes traditionally served with curries to help cool the palate. Examples are banana and coconut, mango chutney, chopped tomato and onion, chopped cucumber and yoghurt, orange segments and so on.

CREAMY POTATO LAMB CASSEROLE

6 chump chops

3 tablespoons seasoned flour

¼ cup (60 ml/2 fl oz) oil

3 onions, sliced

4 tomatoes, peeled and chopped

1 clove garlic, crushed

⅔ cup (155 ml/5 fl oz) white wine

⅔ cup (155 ml/5 fl oz) water

1 chicken stock cube, crumbled

seasonings, to taste

4 zucchini (courgettes), sliced

500 g (1 lb) potatoes, peeled

WHITE SAUCE

30 g (1 oz) butter

1 tablespoon plain (all-purpose) flour

1 cup (250 ml/8 fl oz) milk

¼ cup (30 g/1 oz) grated cheese

Preheat oven to 180°C (350°F).

Dust chops in seasoned flour. Heat oil in a pan. Fry chops until well browned on both sides. Remove, drain and arrange in the base of a shallow ovenproof dish.

In the same oil, sauté onions until transparent. Add tomatoes and garlic. Sauté for 1 minute. Blend in wine, water, stock cube and seasonings. Simmer for 5 minutes.

Blanch zucchinis in boiling water for 1 minute. Arrange over the chops. Pour over tomato mixture.

Blanch the potatoes in boiling water for 3 to 4 minutes. Slice thinly. Arrange the slices, overlapping across the top of the dish.

To Prepare White Sauce: Melt butter in a small saucepan. Blend in flour. Cook for 1 minute, stirring. Remove from heat. Gradually blend in milk. Return to heat. Cook, stirring constantly, until sauce boils and thickens. Simmer for 3 minutes. Stir in half the cheese. Pour sauce over the potatoes. Sprinkle with remaining cheese. Bake for 45 minutes. Serve with salad and crusty bread.

SERVES 4 TO 6

WHITE SAUCE

It is always handy to have a quantity of white sauce prepared and frozen. Thaw completely before using in recipes.

LANCASHIRE HOTPOT

750 g (1½ lb) neck chops, trimmed

3 tablespoons seasoned flour

2 tablespoons oil

4 onions, sliced

750 g (1½ lb) potatoes, sliced

2 lamb's kidneys, trimmed and sliced

250 g (8 oz) mushrooms, sliced

1 parsnip, sliced

2 cups (500 ml/16 fl oz) chicken stock

Preheat oven to 180°C (350°F).

Dust chops in seasoned flour, shaking off excess. Heat oil in a frying pan. Brown chops well on both sides. Drain well. Transfer to a large casserole dish.

Layer onions, potatoes, kidneys, mushrooms and parsnip over chops, finishing with a potato layer. Pour over stock.

Bake, covered, for 2 hours. Remove lid. Bake for a further 30 minutes or until potatoes are golden. Serve with crusty bread.

SERVES 4 TO 6

SPICY ORIENTAL LAMB

Forequarter chops, neck or leg chops or boned leg are ideal for this.

750 g (1½ lb) stewing lamb, cubed

3 tablespoons plain (all-purpose) flour, seasoned

2 tablespoons oil

1 onion, chopped

1 tablespoon grated fresh ginger

2 teaspoons curry powder

8 black peppercorns, crushed

pinch cumin

1 tablespoon tomato paste

2 cups (500 ml/16 fl oz) water

1 teaspoon treacle

1 bay leaf

2 tablespoons desiccated coconut

1 tablespoon cardamom seeds

2 tomatoes, peeled and quartered

Toss lamb in seasoned flour. Heat oil in a large frying pan. Brown meat well on all sides. Transfer to a plate. Keep warm.

Sauté the onion in the same pan until golden brown. Stir in ginger, curry, peppercorns and cumin. Cook for 2 minutes.

Blend in tomato paste followed by water, treacle, bay leaf and coconut. Bring to the boil. Add cardamom seeds.

Return meat to pan. Cover pan and reduce heat. Simmer for 1½ hours or until meat is tender. Garnish with tomatoes. Serve with rice, pappadums and sambals.

SERVES 4 TO 6

COATED MEAT

When coating meat in seasoned flour, always shake off excess to avoid the sauce going lumpy.

DIJON HOTPOT

2 tablespoons oil

6 large lean cutlets

4 carrots, sliced

2 onions, chopped

2 stalks celery, sliced

1 swede, chopped

1¼ cups (315 ml/10 fl oz) water

½ cup (125 ml/4 fl oz) dry white vermouth

1 tablespoon honey

1 tablespoon vinegar

1 chicken stock cube, crumbled

pinch each marjoram, thyme and cumin

seasonings, to taste

1 teaspoon Dijon mustard

Preheat oven to 180°C (350°F).

Heat oil in a frying pan. Fry cutlets until browned. Drain well. Transfer to a casserole dish.

Dijon Hotpot

Add carrots, onions, celery, swede, water and vermouth. Stir in honey, vinegar, stock cube, herbs and seasonings.

Bake, covered, for 1½ hours or until meat is tender. Blend in mustard thoroughly. Serve with rice or potatoes.

SERVES 4 TO 6

BLANCHING VEGETABLES

Blanch vegetables by immersing in boiling water for 30 seconds to 1 minute to partially cook. Refresh under cold running water.

ALGERIAN LAMB CASSEROLE

  2 tablespoons oil

  1 kg (2 lb) cutlets

  4 onions, sliced

  3 potatoes, thinly sliced

  2½ cups (600 ml/70 fl oz) water

  ½ cup (125 ml/4 fl oz) wine

  1 bouquet garni

  1 bay leaf

  pinch cumin

  seasonings, to taste

Preheat oven to 180°C (350°F).

Heat oil in a flameproof dish. Brown cutlets well on both sides. Add onions. Fry until tender.

Add potatoes, water, wine, bouquet garni, bay leaf, cumin and seasonings.

Bake, covered, for 1½ hours or until meat and potatoes are tender. Serve with vegetables of choice.

SERVES 4 TO 6

BARLEY AND LAMB HOTPOT

  1 kg (2 lb) stewing lamb, diced

  1 parsnip, diced

  2 turnips, diced

  2 carrots, diced

  1 onion, chopped

  2 stalks celery, chopped

  6 cups (1½ litres/32 fl oz) water

  1 bouquet garni

  salt and freshly ground black pepper

  ½ cup (90 g/3 oz) barley, soaked overnight in cold water

  1 tablespoon chopped fresh parsley

Above: Algerian Lamb Casserole
Right: Barley and Lamb Hotpot

Blanch lamb in boiling water for 5 minutes. Rinse in cold water and drain.

Place meat in a large saucepan, add parsnip, turnips, carrots, onion, celery, bouquet garni, and salt and pepper to taste. Pour in water and bring to the boil. Simmer for 30 minutes.

Add barley and simmer for 1 hour or until meat and barley are tender, adding extra water if needed. Remove bouquet garni and adjust seasoning to taste. Just before serving, sprinkle with parsley.

SERVES 6

CREAMY CURRIED LAMB

2 tablespoons olive oil

30 g (1 oz) butter or margarine

1 onion, chopped

1 clove garlic, crushed

2 teaspoons curry paste

2 teaspoons grated fresh ginger

1 teaspoon chopped chilli

1 teaspoon ground coriander

½ teaspoon ground cumin

500 g (1 lb) lamb, cubed

250 g (8 oz) button mushrooms

2 tomatoes, chopped

2 zucchini (courgettes), sliced

2 stalks celery, sliced

1 cup (250 ml/8 fl oz) coconut milk

½ cup (125 ml/4 fl oz) white wine

¼ cup (60 ml/2 fl oz) vinegar

rind and juice of 1 lemon

seasonings, to taste

Preheat oven to 180°C (350°F).

Heat oil and butter together in a large frying pan. Sauté onion and garlic until onion is tender.

Mix in curry paste, ginger, chilli, coriander and cumin. Cook gently, stirring, for 5 minutes.

Blend in all remaining ingredients. Transfer mixture to a casserole dish.

Creamy Curried Lamb

Bake for 1 hour or until lamb is tender. Serve with rice, sambals and pappadums.

SERVES 4 TO 6

SERVING CURRIES

Sambals are side dishes served with curries, designed to cool the palate. Examples are: mango chutney, banana tossed in coconut, chopped tomato and onion with lemon juice, and chopped cucumber with natural yoghurt.

GREEK-STYLE LAMB CASSEROLE

The most economical lamb to use is a boned leg.

½ cup (125 ml/4 fl oz) olive oil

2 onions, sliced

1 clove garlic, crushed

4 potatoes, peeled and sliced

1kg/2 lb lamb, trimmed and cubed

1¼ cups (315 ml/10 fl oz) chicken stock

¾ cup (185 ml/6 fl oz) tomato purée

rind and juice of 1 lemon

½ teaspoon dried oregano

seasonings, to taste

1 bay leaf

1 cinnamon stick

Preheat oven to 180°C (350°F).

Heat oil in a large pan. Sauté onions and garlic until onions are tender. Transfer to a plate. Add potatoes to same pan. Sauté until golden. Drain on crumpled kitchen paper. Brown lamb in same pan.

Arrange alternate layers of lamb, onion and potato in a lightly greased casserole dish, finishing with a potato layer.

Blend together stock, tomato purée, lemon rind and juice, oregano and seasonings. Pour over potatoes. Top with bay leaf and cinnamon stick.

Bake for 1 hour or until tender. Remove bay leaf and cinnamon stick before serving. Serve with salad and crusty bread.

SERVES 4 TO 6

HERBS

Always remove bouquet garni, bay leaves and other flavourings from dishes before serving.

Lamb Makeover

*T*o modify this recipe to a healthier version, reducing fat, kilojoules and cholesterol:

Lean lamb is used which is trimmed of any excess fat. Less meat is used and the vegetables have been increased to compensate for this.

Butter is replaced with olive oil.

No salt is used.

Water is used in place of stock reducing salt and fat.

Skin is retained on potatoes, increasing fibre and retaining nutrients.

LAMB WITH NEW POTATOES

2 tablespoons olive oil

500 g (1 lb) lean lamb, trimmed and cubed

4 carrots, sliced

2 onions, sliced

1 clove garlic, crushed

2 tablespoons plain (all-purpose) flour

1 tablespoon tomato paste

3 cups (750 ml/24 fl oz) water

1 bouquet garni

freshly ground black pepper, to taste

500 g (1 lb) new potatoes

1 tablespoon chopped fresh parsley

Preheat oven to 180°C (350°F).

Heat oil in a flameproof casserole dish. Brown meat well on all sides. Add carrots, onions and garlic. Cook, stirring, until lightly browned.

Mix in flour. Cook, stirring, for 1 minute. Stir in tomato paste. Remove from heat. Gradually blend in water. Return to heat. Stir constantly until sauce boils and thickens.

Add bouquet garni and pepper. Bake, covered, for 1½ hours.

Parboil potatoes for 10 minutes. Stir into casserole. Bake for a further 30 minutes. Sprinkle with parsley. Serve with salad and crusty bread.

SERVES 4 TO 6

Pork

Pork lends itself well to salting, smoking and curing, so many of the recipes in this section call for ham, gammon, sausages or bacon.

It is a good idea to trim pork well before using and skim off any fat that rises to the surface during cooking.

Glasses from Corso de Fiori, Darlinghurst
Fabric from Les Olivades, Double Bay
Tray from Home & Garden on the Mall, Skygarden, Sydney
Napkins from Made n' Earth, Mid City Centre, Sydney

HAM AND APPLE BAKE

- 30 g (1 oz) butter or margarine
- 2 onions, sliced
- 2 apples, peeled, cored and sliced
- 4 to 6 thick ham steaks
- 2 tablespoons plain (all-purpose) flour
- 1¼ cups (315 ml/10 fl oz) dry cider, apple juice or white wine
- ½ cup (125 ml/4 fl oz) chicken stock
- 315 g (10 oz) canned corn kernels, drained
- 125 g (4 oz) mushrooms, sliced
- ¼ cup (30 g/1 oz) raisins
- ½ teaspoon mustard powder
- seasonings, to taste

Preheat oven to 180°C (350°F).

Melt butter in a frying pan. Sauté onions and apples until tender. Add ham. Brown well on both sides. Transfer mixture to a casserole dish.

Blend flour into same pan. Cook 1 minute. Add cider and stock. Heat, stirring constantly, until mixture boils and thickens. Stir in all remaining ingredients. Simmer for 1 minute.

Pour sauce into casserole dish with ham. Bake, covered, for 45 minutes. Serve with jacket potatoes and salad.

SERVES 4 TO 6

COOKED MEAT

Check if whole pieces of meat are cooked by inserting a fork or skewer into the largest muscle of the joint. If it comes out easily, it is cooked. The juices will also run clear.

PORK IN CIDER

White wine may be used in place of cider.

- ½ cup (125 ml/4 fl oz) oil
- 2 onions, chopped
- 2 carrots, chopped
- 2 spring onions, chopped
- 1 stalk celery, sliced
- 1 clove garlic, crushed
- ½ cup (60 g/2 oz) plain (all-purpose) flour
- 1 cup (250 ml/8 fl oz) dry cider or apple juice
- 3 tomatoes, peeled and chopped
- 315 g (10 oz) canned creamed corn
- 1 bouquet garni
- seasonings, to taste
- 6 pork chops, trimmed
- 1 tablespoon chopped fresh parsley

Preheat oven to 180°C (350°F).

Heat half the oil in a large frying pan. Sauté onions, carrots, spring onions, celery and garlic until tender. Sprinkle over half the flour. Cook, stirring, for 1 minute.

Blend in cider and tomatoes. Bring to the boil, stirring constantly. Stir in the corn, bouquet garni and seasonings. Simmer for 10 minutes.

Dust chops in remaining flour, shaking off excess. Heat remaining oil in a pan. Cook chops until well browned on both sides. Drain well. Place in a casserole dish.

Pour over sauce. Bake, covered, for 30 minutes or until meat is tender. Sprinkle with parsley. Serve with boiled new potatoes.

SERVES 4 TO 6

Picture previous pages: Spiced Gammon Casserole (page 35), Pork Chops with Mushroom Cream Sauce (page 42)

SEASONED FLOUR

Seasoned flour is plain flour flavoured with seasonings of your choice. It may be salt, pepper, herbs, mustard powder or even grated cheese.

PORK AND APPLE CRUMBLE

- 60 g (2 oz) butter
- 2 onions, sliced
- 250 g (8 oz) apples, peeled and sliced

BASE

- 500 g (1 lb) pork fillet
- ¼ cup (30 g/1 oz) seasoned plain (all-purpose) flour
- ⅔ cup (160 ml/5 fl oz) cider
- 1¾ cups (420 ml/14 fl oz) chicken stock
- 45 g (1½ oz) raisins
- 1 bouquet garni

TOPPING

- 1¼ cups (155 g/5 oz) plain (all-purpose) flour, sifted
- 45 g (1½ oz) butter or margarine
- 1 teaspoon dried sage
- ½ onion, grated
- salt and freshly ground black pepper

Preheat oven to 180°C (350°F).

Melt half the butter in a fry pan, sauté onion and apple 2 to 3 minutes. Remove, place in casserole dish.

Toss pork in flour. Melt remaining butter in frypan and fry pork until evenly browned.

place in casserole, cover with cider and stock. Add raisins and bouquet garni. Cover and bake for 30 minutes.

Increase oven temperature to 200°C (400°F).

To Prepare Topping: Rub butter into flour, stir in sage and onion and seasonings. Place pork mixture in pie dish, add sufficient gravy to just cover pork.

Sprinkle with topping. Bake for 20 to 30 minutes. Reserve any excess gravy to serve with crumble.

SERVES 4

FRESH ROSEMARY PORK

- 125 g (4 oz) butter or margarine
- 1kg (2 lb) boned shoulder or loin of pork
- 1 onion, chopped
- 1 carrot, chopped
- 1 stalk celery, chopped
- 350 g (11 oz) mushrooms, thickly sliced
- 1¼ cups (315 ml/10 fl oz) water
- ½ cup (125 ml/4 fl oz) dry white wine
- 2 sprigs rosemary
- 1 clove garlic, crushed

Preheat oven to 180°C (350°F).

Heat half of the butter in a large frying pan. Brown meat well on all sides. Drain well. Transfer to a casserole dish.

Sauté onion, carrot and celery in same pan until tender. Stir in mushrooms. Sauté for 2 minutes.

Pour vegetables over meat with water, wine rosemary and garlic. Bake, covered, for 1½ hours (or until meat is cooked when tested). Serve with vegetables in season.

SERVES 4 TO 6

PREPARING MUSHROOMS

Mushrooms do not need washing or peeling. Simply trim the base of the stalk if necessary and chop as directed — or use whole. Add them towards the end of cooking time so they do not overcook.

SPICED GAMMON CASSEROLE

- 1 tablespoon oil
- 750 g (1½ lb) thick ham steaks or lean gammon, cubed
- 1 onion, sliced
- 2 stalks celery, sliced
- 1 cup (155 g/5 oz) long grain rice
- 2 cups (500 ml/16 fl oz) chicken stock
- 425 g (13½ oz) canned tomatoes, chopped
- 1 bay leaf
- ¼ teaspoon each oregano and marjoram
- pinch cinnamon
- seasonings, to taste
- 250 g (8 oz) frozen broad beans
- 125 g (4 oz) button mushrooms

Preheat oven to 180°C (350°F).

Heat oil in a frying pan. Fry ham until sealed on all sides. Remove with a slotted spoon to a casserole dish. Sauté onion and celery in same pan until onion is tender. Stir in the rice. Cook, stirring, for 3 minutes.

Stir in stock, tomatoes, bay leaf, oregano, marjoram, cinnamon and seasonings. Bring to the boil. Pour over ham.

Bake, covered, for 1 hour, forking through rice occasionally. More stock may be added if mixture becomes too dry.

Mix in beans and mushrooms. Bake for a further 30 minutes. Serve with boiled new potatoes.

SERVES 4 TO 6

MAKING STOCK

1 stock cube crumbled into 1 cup (250 ml/8 fl oz) water is the usual ratio for stock. More cubes may be added if a stronger flavour is desired.

PORK

Pork is widely available all over the world. It is high in fat but there are now leaner cuts on the market. The rib loin is extremely high in fat. Cuts with much lower amounts of fat include the rump, round and topside. Pork, like other meats is a valuable source of protein, iron and zinc and other nutrients.

Pork should never be undercooked. It can be refrigerated, though should be covered and eaten within a couple of days. It can also be frozen. Pork is used in a great variety of ways depending on the cut. It can be stir-fried, braised, roasted, used in stroganoffs, curries and many other dishes.

FARMHOUSE SOUP

60 g (2 oz) butter or margarine

2 carrots, diced

2 turnips, diced

2 leeks, sliced

2 stalks celery, sliced

500 g (1 lb) bacon joint, rind removed

water

8 cups (2 litres/70 fl oz) chicken stock

½ cabbage, shredded

seasonings, to taste

155 g (5 oz) green beans, sliced

155 g (5 oz) peas

2 potatoes, peeled and chopped

¼ cup (60 g/2 oz) grated Gruyère cheese

croutons

Melt butter in a large saucepan. Sauté carrots, turnips, leeks and celery until tender.

Place bacon in a saucepan. Cover with water. Bring to the boil. Reduce heat. Simmer for 10 minutes. Drain well. Rinse in cold water.

Add stock to vegetables with bacon, cabbage and seasonings. Simmer, covered, for 1 hour.

Sausage and Red Lentil Soup

Stir in beans, peas and potatoes. Simmer for a further 20 minutes. Remove bacon from soup. Cut into cubes. Return to soup. Serve soup sprinkled with cheese and croutons.

To Prepare Croutons: cut crusts from 'day old' bread. Cut into 1 cm (½ in) cubes. Fry in equal quantities of butter and oil until golden. Drain on crumpled kitchen paper. Freeze in an airtight container if liked. Reheat in the oven before serving.

SERVES 4 TO 6

SAUSAGE AND RED LENTIL SOUP

375 g (12 oz) red lentils, washed

water

¼ cup (60 ml/2 fl oz) olive oil

500 g (1 lb) pork sausage, cut into bite-sized pieces

1 onion, chopped

2 cloves garlic, crushed

1 green capsicum (pepper), seeded and chopped

1kg (2 lb) tomatoes, peeled and chopped

2 cups (500 ml/16 fl oz) beef stock

1 tablespoon Worcestershire sauce

¼ teaspoon ground oregano

seasonings, to taste

Place lentils in a large saucepan with enough water to come 2½ cm (1 in) above the lentils. Bring to the boil. Reduce heat. Simmer for 25 to 30 minutes or until lentils are tender. Drain well. Set aside.

Heat oil in the same saucepan. Cook sausage until well browned. Transfer to a plate. Add onion and garlic. Sauté until onion is tender.

Stir in the capsicum. Sauté for a further 2 minutes. Add the lentils, sausage and all remaining ingredients to pan. Simmer, covered, for 45 minutes.

SERVES 4 TO 6

Right: Farmhouse Soup

MINESTRONE

Minestrone is a hearty soup, filled with wholesome vegetables, made throughout Italy. The Milanese claim to have invented it.

- 8 rashers (250 g/8 oz) bacon
- 1 bunch fresh parsley, finely chopped
- 1 stalk celery, chopped
- 1 clove garlic, crushed
- 125 g (4 oz) green beans, chopped
- 3 tomatoes, peeled and chopped
- 2 potatoes, chopped
- 2 carrots, chopped
- 1 zucchini (courgette), chopped
- 1 cup (180 g/6 oz) dried borlotti beans, soaked overnight and drained
- seasonings, to taste
- water
- 1 cup (30 g/1 oz) shredded cabbage
- 1 cup (155 g/5 oz) long grain rice
- grated Parmesan cheese

Remove rind from bacon. Place in a large saucepan with chopped bacon, parsley, celery and garlic. Cook gently for 5 minutes, stirring occasionally.

Add green beans, tomatoes, potatoes, carrots, zucchini, dried beans and seasonings to pan. Cover with water. Bring to the boil. Reduce heat. Simmer, covered, for 1 hour. Add more water if necessary.

Stir in cabbage. Simmer for a further 30 minutes. Blend in rice. Simmer until rice is cooked and beans are tender. Remove bacon rind. Sprinkle with Parmesan cheese. Serve with crusty bread.

SERVES 4 TO 6

SPICY PORK CASSEROLE

- 30 g (1 oz) butter or margarine
- 500 g (1 lb) pork sausages
- 2 apples, peeled, cored and sliced
- 1 onion, sliced
- ½ cup (125 ml/4 fl oz) cider, juice or white wine
- 1 tablespoon tomato paste
- 1 chicken stock cube, crumbled
- 1 bouquet garni
- pinch each mixed spice and cinnamon
- seasonings, to taste
- 2 teaspoons cornflour
- ¼ cup (60 ml/2 fl oz) water

Preheat oven to 180°C (350°F).

Heat butter in a flameproof casserole dish. Cook sausages, apples and onion until sausages are brown and onion is tender.

Blend in cider, tomato paste, stock cube, bouquet garni, spices and seasonings. Bake, covered, for about 35 minutes.

Blend cornflour with water to form a smooth paste. Stir into casserole on top of the stove. Cook, stirring constantly, until mixture boils and thickens. Simmer for 3 minutes. Serve with jacket potatoes, pumpkin and peas.

SERVES 4 TO 6

FLAMEPROOF DISHES

If flameproof casserole dishes are unavailable, brown meat and sauté vegetables in a frying pan and transfer to a casserole dish for baking. Alternatively, the dish may be cooked in a saucepan on top of the stove, for the ultimate in one pot cooking.

PORK STEW SERVED WITH HORSERADISH

- 60 g (2 oz) butter or margarine
- 1¼ kg (2½ lb) shoulder pork, cubed
- 4 onions, chopped
- 4 carrots, sliced
- 1 turnip, cut into strips
- 2 whole cloves
- 1 bay leaf
- ½ teaspoon thyme
- seasonings, to taste
- beef stock or water
- 1kg (2 lb) potatoes, peeled and diced
- grated fresh horseradish

Preheat oven to 180°C (350°F).

Melt butter in a frying pan. Sauté pork until well browned on all sides. Transfer to a casserole dish using a slotted spoon.

Add onions, carrots, turnip, cloves, bay leaf, thyme and seasonings to casserole. Pour over enough stock to just cover the ingredients.

Bake, covered, for 1½ hours or until pork is tender.

Steam, microwave or boil potatoes until tender. Serve the stew over the potatoes. Top with a generous sprinkling of horseradish.

SERVES 4 TO 6

PORK VINDALOO

2 onions, chopped

2 cloves garlic, crushed

1 red capsicum (pepper), seeded and chopped

2 tablespoons oil

2 teaspoons vinegar

1 tablespoon curry powder

2 teaspoons ground ginger

seasonings, to taste

500 g (1 lb) pork spare ribs, trimmed and halved

1 cup (250 ml/8 fl oz) water

Combine onions, garlic, red capsicum, oil and vinegar. Blend in curry powder, ginger and seasonings. Mix well.

Coat meat with this mixture. Place in a large saucepan with the water. Simmer, covered, for 2 hours.

Serve with rice cooked with a pinch of turmeric, sambals and pappadums.

SERVES 4

SAMBALS

These are side dishes which make good accompaniments for curries and vindaloos. Try some of these ideas:

- Mix low fat natural yoghurt with chopped cucumber and fresh mint.

- Combine sliced bananas with chopped chilli, and lemon juice, or use apple instead or banana.

- Mix 1 cup (250 ml/8 fl oz) coconut milk with chopped onion, crushed garlic and chilli powder.

- Make up your own choose a selection of vegetables, blanch them and combine with chopped chillies, lemon juice, a little oil and desiccated coconut.

CRUSHED GARLIC

Crush garlic cloves by chopping finely and then pressing with the blade of a knife to crush. A little salt sprinkled onto the clove before crushing will absorb any garlic juice that escapes. Alternatively, use a garlic press.

PORK GOULASH

750 g (1½ lb) pork fillet, diced

4 tablespoons paprika

40 g (1½ oz) butter

1 onion, sliced

1 red capsicum (pepper), seeded and sliced

1 green capsicum (pepper), seeded and sliced

5 tablespoons plain (all-purpose) flour

¾ cup (180 ml/6 fl oz) chicken stock

150 g (5 oz) button mushrooms

8 tomatoes, peeled and chopped

1 cup (250 ml/8 fl oz) sour cream

1 tablespoon chopped fresh dill or chives, to garnish

Sprinkle pork with 2 tablespoons paprika. Melt butter in a frypan and brown meat, then remove and drain.

Sauté onion and capsicum until tender and remove from pan. Stir in flour and remaining paprika, cook for 2 minutes. Stir in stock and bring to the boil.

Place pork, sauce, mushrooms and tomatoes in a saucepan. Cover and simmer for 45 minutes. Stir half the cream through the dish just before serving. Garnish with a dollop of sour cream and a sprinkle of dill or chives. Serve with boiled baby potatoes and any green vegetables.

SERVES 4

SPICY HOTPOT WITH CORN AND CHIVES

500 g (1 lb) pork sausages

155 g (5 oz) butter

500 g (1 lb) frankfurts

2 onions, chopped

1 red capsicum (pepper), seeded and chopped

1 green capsicum (pepper), seeded and chopped

1½ cups (250 g/8 oz) long grain rice

chilli powder, to taste

4 cups (1 litre/1 pt 12 fl oz) chicken stock

2 tablespoons tomato paste

1 cup (170 g/5½ oz) canned corn kernels, drained

freshly ground black pepper

4 tomatoes, cut into wedges

2 teaspoons snipped chives, to garnish

Boil pork sausages in water for 10 minutes (to remove excess fat) and drain.

Melt butter and fry frankfurts and sausages over medium heat for 4 to 5 minutes, shaking pan to prevent sticking. Remove sausages from pan and cut into chunky pieces.

Sauté onions and capsicum in pan until onions are lightly golden. Add rice and chilli powder and cook over gentle heat 2 to 3 minutes, stirring all the time.

Add stock, tomato paste, corn, sausage pieces and seasoning. Bring to the boil, stir well, reduce heat and simmer gently 15 minutes until rice is tender and liquid absorbed.

Add tomatoes to pan for the last 5 minutes of cooking. Sprinkle with chives and serve.

SERVES 4 TO 6

Paprika Pork Casserole

PAPRIKA PORK CASSEROLE

500 g (1 lb) pork shoulder, diced

180 g (6 oz) button mushrooms, sliced

4 sticks celery, chopped

250 g (8 oz) zucchini (courgettes), chopped

2 tomatoes, peeled and chopped

1 green capsicum (pepper), seeded and sliced

1 to 2 onions, chopped

2 tablespoons paprika

1¼ cups (310 ml/10 fl oz) chicken stock

plain (all-purpose) flour

Preheat oven to 180°C (350°F).

Place pork in ovenproof dish with mushrooms, celery, zucchini, tomatoes, capsicum and onion. Sprinkle with paprika.

Pour over stock, cover and bake for 1¾ to 2 hours.

Mix flour with a little cold water and stir into casserole to thicken. Serve casserole hot.

SERVES 4 TO 6

MUSHROOMS

To clean mushrooms, wipe with a damp cloth. Don't wash under water and don't peel the skin off as this is the most nutritious part of the mushroom.

CREAMY PORK WITH WHITE WINE

1 green capsicum (pepper),
   seeded and chopped

1 red capsicum (pepper), seeded
   and chopped

90 g (3 oz) butter or margarine

125 g (4 oz) button mushrooms,
   sliced

½ cup (60 g/2 oz) plain
   (all-purpose) flour

1¼ cups (315 ml/10 fl oz)
   chicken stock

½ cup (125 ml/4 fl oz) milk

½ cup (125 ml/4 fl oz) cream

500 g (1 lb) cooked pork, cubed

1 cup (250 ml/8 fl oz) white wine

2 tablespoons brandy

seasonings, to taste

Blanch capsicums in boiling water for 1 minute. Drain well. Set aside.

Melt butter in a large frying pan. Sauté mushrooms for 3 minutes. Blend in flour. Cook, stirring, for 1 minute.

Remove from heat. Gradually blend in stock. Return to heat. Bring to the boil, stirring constantly. Simmer for 3 minutes. Stir in milk and cream. Simmer for 2 minutes.

Stir in pork, capsicum, wine, brandy and seasonings. Heat gently. Serve with boiled rice and salad.

SERVES 4 TO 6

Creamy Pork with White Wine

Sauté mushrooms in butter.

Thicken with flour.

Add pork, capsicum, wine and brandy.

PORK CHOPS WITH MUSHROOM CREAM SAUCE

4 to 6 pork chops, trimmed

2 tablespoons plain (all-purpose) flour

30 g (1 oz) butter or margarine

1 onion, chopped

1½ cups (90 g/3 oz) sliced mushrooms

1¼ cups (315 ml/10 fl oz) cider or white wine

¼ cup (60 ml/2 fl oz) cream

seasonings, to taste

1 tablespoon chopped fresh parsley

Dust chops lightly in half of the flour. Shake off excess. Melt butter in a large frying pan. Fry chops until well browned on both sides and cooked. Transfer to a plate. Keep warm.

Sauté onion in same pan until tender. Add mushrooms. Sauté for 3 minutes. Stir in remaining flour. Cook 1 minute. Remove pan from heat. Gradually blend in cider.

Return pan to heat. Cook, stirring constantly, until sauce boils and thickens. Stir in cream and seasonings. Return chops to pan. Heat gently for 5 minutes. Sprinkle with parsley. Serve with vegetables of choice.

SERVES 4 TO 6

STORING AND FREEZING PORK

Remove wrapping from pork and store on a rack over a dish in the refrigerator. Make sure it is covered loosely – use foil or greaseproof paper. Use within 2 days. To freeze pork, trim excess fat and wrap pieces indivdually in plastic wrap or freezer bag with the air pressed out. The length of time pork can be frozen for depends on the cut.

ORIENTAL SPARE RIBS

Pork is the most popular meat eaten in China and in many other Asian countries. This simple recipe brings you the taste of the Orient.

1 kg (2 lb) pork spare ribs, trimmed

1¼ cups (315 ml/10 fl oz) water

½ cup (125 ml/4 fl oz) vinegar

½ cup (125 ml/4 fl oz) tomato sauce

½ cup (90 g/3 oz) brown sugar

1½ teaspoons soy sauce

3 tablespoons cornflour (cornstarch)

¼ cup (60 ml/2 fl oz) water

Preheat oven to 180°C (350°F).

Place spare ribs in a baking dish. Pour over combined water and vinegar. Bake for 1 hour.

Skim off any fat from liquid. Strain liquid into a saucepan.

Blend the combined tomato sauce, brown sugar and soy into liquid. Mix cornflour with water to form a smooth paste. Blend into mixture. Heat, stirring, until mixture boils and thickens.

Pour the sauce over the spare ribs. Bake for a further 30 minutes or until pork is golden brown. Serve with rice or noodles.

SERVES 4 TO 6

LOW FAT

If you are counting kilojoules, then don't toss meat in flour. Simply brown in olive oil.

PORK PORTUGUESE

1½ kg (3 lb) diced pork

3 tablespoons seasoned flour

2 tablespoons oil

2 onions, chopped

3 stalks celery, chopped

2 tomatoes, peeled and chopped

1 green capsicum (pepper), seeded and chopped

1¼ cups (315 ml/10 fl oz) water

1¼ cups (315 ml/10 fl oz) dry white wine

2 tablespoons tomato paste

1 clove garlic, crushed

1 bouquet garni

seasonings, to taste

1½ tablespoons cornflour (cornstarch)

Preheat oven to 180°C (350°F).

Dust pork in seasoned flour. Shake off excess. Heat oil in a frying pan. Cook pork until well browned. Transfer to a casserole dish.

In the same pan, sauté onions until golden. Add celery, tomatoes and green capsicum. Sauté for 5 minutes.

Transfer the vegetable mixture to the casserole dish. Stir in water, wine, tomato paste, garlic, bouquet garni and seasonings. Bake, covered, for 1½ hours or until meat is tender.

Blend cornflour with a little water to form a smooth paste. Stir into casserole. Return to oven for a further 15 minutes. Serve with rice and crusty bread.

SERVES 4 TO 6

SIMMERED PORK WITH GOLDEN SAUCE

1 kg (2 lb) boned pork from the leg or loin

60 g (2 oz) butter

1 onion, finely chopped

1 carrot, finely chopped

1 celery stalk, finely chopped

2 sprigs parsley

salt and freshly ground black pepper

1½ cups (375 ml/12 fl oz) milk

Tie the meat to form a large sausage. In a deep pan, melt butter and sauté onion, carrot and celery, until translucent. Place parsley on top of this mixture, then the meat. Brown it to seal all the juices, season, pour the milk over and put lid on pan. Cook slowly for about 2 hours without stirring.

At the end of the cooking, the milk will form a lovely golden sauce around the meat. The only point at which this dish needs watching is towards the end of the cooking, because if the milk evaporates too much, it may stick to the pan and burn. Eat it hot or cold, with the sauce poured over it.

(This dish can also be cooked in the oven. Just reduce the quantity of milk by half.)

SERVES 4

ECONOMICAL DISHES

Choose the inexpensive, tougher cuts of meat. It is not worth purchasing the newer cuts of beef, lamb or pork – these are best used for other cooking methods such as pan-frying, grilling and stir fries.

Pork Makeover

*T*o modify this recipe to a healthier version, reducing fat, kilojoules and cholesterol:

Olive oil is used in place of butter.

Trimmed, lean, pork pieces are used. These are readily available from your butcher.

The amount of pork is halved and tomatoes and carrots added to compensate for this.

No salt is used.

Sour cream is replaced by low fat versions of cream or yoghurt. This of course may be avoided altogether.

PORK GOULASH WITH CARAWAY SEEDS

2 tablespoons olive oil

4 onions, sliced

1 clove garlic, crushed

1 tablespoon chopped fresh dill

1 teaspoon caraway seeds

freshly ground black pepper, to taste

750 g (1½ lb) lean pork pieces

425 g (13½ oz) canned tomatoes, chopped

2 carrots, sliced

½ cup (125 ml/4 fl oz) water

850 g (1 lb 11 oz) canned sauerkraut

1 tablespoon paprika

½ cup (125 ml/4 fl oz) reduced cream or low fat yoghurt (optional)

Heat oil in a flameproof casserole dish. Sauté onions and garlic until golden brown. Stir in dill, caraway seeds and pepper. Cook for 1 minute.

Stir in pork, tomatoes, carrots and water. Simmer, covered, for 30 minutes. Add more water, 1 tablespoon at a time, if required.

Mix in sauerkraut and paprika. Cook, covered, over a very low heat for 30 minutes or until pork is tender. Stir in reduced cream or yoghurt. Heat through gently. Serve with potatoes.

SERVES 4 TO 6

Veal

*H*aving a greater delicacy of flavour than beef, and a much lower fat content than pork or lamb, veal lends itself to rich, creamy dishes.

This section shows the versatility of veal through traditional favourites as well as newer ideas.

Servingware and glassware from Home & Garden on the Mall, Skygarden, Sydney
Fabrics from Les Olivades, Double Bay

VEAL MOZZARELLA

Ask your butcher to flatten the veal steaks or do it yourself by placing veal between 2 sheets of plastic wrap and pounding with a meat mallet.

750 g (1½ lb) veal steaks, flattened

juice 1 lemon

3 tablespoons seasoned flour

30 g (1 oz) butter or margarine

1 tablespoon oil

425 g (13½ oz) canned tomato soup

2 tablespoons dry vermouth

1 teaspoon dried oregano

seasonings, to taste

185 g (6 oz) thinly sliced mozzarella cheese

chopped fresh mint

Preheat oven to 180°C (350°F).

Cut veal into serving sized pieces. Place pieces on a plate. Pour over lemon juice. Allow to stand for 1 hour.

Pat veal dry. Dust in flour, shaking off excess. Heat butter and oil together in a frying pan. Brown veal quickly on both sides. Place veal in a casserole dish with combined tomato soup, vermouth, oregano and seasonings. Bake, covered, for 20 minutes.

Arrange mozzarella slices on top of casserole. Bake for a further 10 minutes or until cheese has melted. Sprinkle with mint. Serve with salad and crusty bread.

SERVES 4 TO 6

Picture previous pages: Veal and Spinach Soup (page 46), Veal with Yoghurt (page 48)

SPINACH AND VEAL SOUP

2 tablespoons olive oil

750 g (1½ lb) veal knuckles

6 potatoes, cubed

3 onions, sliced

8 cups (2 litres/3½ pt) water

1 bunch spinach, washed, centre veins removed and chopped

4 tomatoes, washed, peeled and chopped

pinch nutmeg

seasonings, to taste

grated Parmesan cheese

Heat oil in a large saucepan. Brown veal well on all sides. Remove from pan. Sauté potatoes and onions until onions are tender.

Return veal to pan with water. Bring to the boil. Simmer, covered, for 1½ hours.

Remove knuckles from soup. Cut meat from bones. Chop roughly.

Return to soup with spinach, tomatoes and seasonings. Simmer for a further 10 minutes. Sprinkle with cheese. Serve with crusty bread.

SERVES 4 TO 6

VEAL GOULASH SOUP

30 g (1 oz) butter or margarine

1 onion, chopped

1 clove garlic, crushed

2 potatoes, chopped

1 green capsicum (pepper), seeded and chopped

250 g (8 oz) minced veal

440 g (14 oz) canned tomato soup

2 cups (500 ml/16 fl oz) water

1 teaspoon paprika

½ teaspoon caraway seeds

seasonings, to taste

sour cream

Melt butter in a large saucepan. Sauté onion and garlic until onion is tender.

Add potatoes and capsicum. Sauté for 1 minute. Stir in mince. Brown well, breaking up with a spoon as it cooks.

Blend in soup, water, paprika, caraway seeds and seasonings. Simmer for 20 minutes, stirring occasionally. Top with a dollop of sour cream. Serve with crusty bread.

SERVES 4 TO 6

VEAL SOUP WITH EGG NOODLES

2 tablespoons oil

1 kg (2 lb) veal knuckles

2 carrots, chopped

2 stalks celery, sliced

2 potatoes, chopped

1 leek, sliced

1 clove garlic, crushed

8 cups (2 litres/70 fl oz) water

425 g (13½ oz) canned tomatoes, chopped

125 g (4 oz) egg noodles

1 cup (125 g/4 oz) frozen peas

seasonings, to taste

Heat oil in a large saucepan. Brown veal well on all sides. Transfer to a plate.

Sauté carrots, celery, potatoes, leek and garlic in same pan until tender.

Return knuckles to pan with water and tomatoes. Bring to the boil. Reduce heat. Simmer, covered, for 1½ hours or until veal is tender.

Remove meat from knuckles. Return meat to saucepan with remaining ingredients. Discard bones. Simmer for a further 15 to 20 minutes or until noodles are tender. Serve with crusty rolls.

SERVES 4 TO 6

VEAL WITH OLIVES AND PROSCIUTTO

2 tablespoons oil

30 g (1 oz) butter

1 kg nut of veal

1 cup (250 ml/8 fl oz) dry white wine

30 g (1 oz0 butter, extra

4 spring onions, ends and tops removed

4 slices prosciutto, cut into pieces

8 sage leaves

1 tablespoon plain (all-purpose) flour

1 cup (250 ml/8 fl oz) veal stock

125 g (4 oz) green olives

cracked black pepper

Preheat oven to 180°C (350°F).

Heat oil and butter in baking tray, add veal and cook in oven for 30 minutes. Add wine and cook a further 30 minutes.

Remove veal from oven, strain off liquid and reserve. Return veal to oven to keep warm while making sauce.

Melt extra butter in pan and cook spring onions and prosciutto until onions are golden and prosciutto is crisp. Add sage, cook further 1 minute. Using a slotted spoon, remove spring onions, prosciutto and sage from pan and set aside.

Add flour to pan and stir until golden brown. Add reserved liquid and veal stock and stir until sauce boils and thickens. Reduce heat, return spring onions, season with black pepper and simmer 3 minutes.

Remove veal from oven, slice, arrange on platter or serving plates and spoon on sauce.

SERVES 4

MEDITERRANEAN VEAL STEW

3 tablespoons oil

750 g (1½ lb) shoulder of veal, trimmed and cubed

3 onions, chopped

3 tablespoons (all-purpose) plain flour

500 g (1 lb) tomatoes, peeled and chopped

2 cups (250 g/8 oz) frozen peas

1 cup (250 ml/8 fl oz) chicken stock

2 green capsicums (peppers), seeded and sliced

2 cloves garlic, crushed

juice 1 lemon

seasonings, to taste

125 g (4 oz) pitted green olives, chopped

½ cup (125 ml/4 fl oz) cream

Heat oil in a large pan. Lightly brown the meat and the onions.

Add the flour. Cook, stirring, for 1 minute. Blend in tomatoes, peas, stock, capsicum, garlic, lemon juice and seasonings. Bring to the boil. Simmer for 25 minutes.

Stir in olives. Simmer for another 15 minutes. Blend in cream. Heat gently for 5 minutes. Serve with rice, salad and crusty bread.

SERVES 4 TO 6

ARTICHOKES

There are two types of artichoke – globe and Jerusalem. Canned artichokes are convenient to use in a recipe but if you wish to use fresh ones, here's how you prepare them: Cut off the stalk from the base. Trim the stem end to expose the white base. Cut the top off to expose the pink tips of the choke. Scoop out choke, leaving behind the heart. Put it in lemon juice to prevent browning.

LESS FAT

After browning, drain meat on crumpled kitchen paper to remove excess fat before adding it to casserole.

VEAL WITH ARTICHOKE HEARTS

4 veal shanks or veal knuckles, cut into 6 cm (2½ in) pieces

3 tablespoons seasoned flour

30 g (1 oz) butter or margarine

2 carrots, sliced

2 stalks celery, sliced

1 onion, sliced

2 cloves garlic, crushed

1 cup (250 ml/8 fl oz) water

½ cup (125 ml/4 fl oz) dry white wine

4 tomatoes, peeled and chopped

1 tablespoon tomato paste

1 bay leaf

¼ teaspoon dried rosemary

seasonings, to taste

425 g (13½ oz) canned artichoke hearts, drained

rind and juice of 1 lemon

1 tablespoon chopped fresh parsley

Dust veal in flour, shaking off excess. Melt butter in a large, heavy-based saucepan. Brown meat well on all sides. Transfer to a plate.

Sauté carrots, celery, onion and garlic in same pan until tender. Return meat to pan with water, wine, tomatoes, tomato paste, herbs and seasonings.

Bring to the boil. Reduce heat. Simmer, covered, for 1 hour or until meat is tender.

Stir in remaining ingredients. Simmer for 10 minutes. Sprinkle with parsley. Serve with rice or noodles, salad and crusty bread.

SERVES 4 TO 6

CREAMY VEAL WITH MUSHROOMS

750 g (1½ lb) veal, cubed

2 onions, chopped

1½ cups (375 ml/12 fl oz) water

½ cup (125 ml/4 fl oz) dry white wine

1 bay leaf

¼ teaspoon ground thyme

seasonings, to taste

30 g (1 oz) butter or margarine

3 tablespoons plain (all-purpose) flour

2 tablespoons milk

125 g (4 oz) button mushrooms, sliced

chopped fresh parsley

Preheat oven to 180°C (350°F).

Place veal, onions, water, wine, herbs and seasonings in a casserole dish. Bake, covered, for 1¼ hours or until meat is tender. Strain liquid from meat and reserve.

Melt butter in a small saucepan. Blend in flour. Cook for 1 minute.

Creamy Veal with Mushrooms

Remove from heat. Gradually blend in reserved liquid and milk to make a smooth paste.

Place mushrooms in casserole dish with veal. Pour over sauce. Bake for a further 20 minutes. Sprinkle with parsley. Serve with vegetables in season.

SERVES 4 TO 6

VEAL WITH YOGHURT

30 g (2 oz) butter or margarine

750 g (1½ lb) veal steaks, sliced

2 onions, chopped

1½ cups (375 ml/12 fl oz) chicken stock

1 tablespoon paprika

seasonings, to taste

1 tablespoon oil

2 green capsicums (peppers), seeded and chopped

4 tomatoes, peeled and chopped

1½ cups (375 ml/12 fl oz) natural yoghurt

Melt butter in a large frying pan. Sauté the veal with the onions until veal is lightly browned.

Add stock, paprika and seasonings. Simmer, covered, for 20 minutes.

Heat oil in a separate pan. Cook capsicums over a low heat for 10 to 15 minutes. Add the tomatoes. Cook for a further 10 minutes, stirring constantly.

Stir tomato mixture into meat mixture with yoghurt. Heat through gently. Do not boil. Serve with rice or noodles and salad.

SERVES 4 TO 6

VEAL HOTPOT

750 g (1½ lb) veal, cubed

2 tablespoons plain (all-purpose) flour

2 tablespoons oil

4 rashers (125 g/4 oz) rindless bacon, chopped

1 onion, chopped

1 red or green capsicum (pepper), seeded and chopped

2 potatoes, peeled and quartered

1 carrot, sliced

1 clove garlic, crushed

2 cups (500 ml/16 fl oz) chicken stock

4 tomatoes, peeled and quartered

1 tablespoon tomato paste

1 bouquet garni

¼ teaspoon paprika

seasonings, to taste

Preheat oven to 180°C (350°F).

Dust veal in flour, shaking off excess. Heat oil in a frying pan. Brown meat well. Transfer to a casserole dish.

Sauté bacon, onion and capsicum in same pan until bacon is golden. Add potatoes, carrot and garlic. Sauté for a further 2 minutes. Spoon over veal with all remaining ingredients.

Bake, covered, for 1 hour or until veal is tender. Serve with pasta.

SERVES 4 TO 6

VEAL TOMATO CASSEROLE

3 tablespoons oil

750 g (1½ lb) veal, cubed

4 onions, finely chopped

2 cloves garlic, crushed

4 tomatoes, peeled, seeded and chopped

½ cup (125 ml/4 fl oz) dry white wine

Veal Hotpot

seasonings, to taste

2 cups (500 ml/16 fl oz) chicken stock

Heat oil in a large pan. Sauté veal until well browned. Add the onions and garlic. Sauté until onion is tender.

Stir in tomatoes, wine and seasonings. Simmer for 5 minutes.

Pour in stock. Bring to the boil. Reduce heat to very low. Simmer gently, covered, for 1 to 1½ hours, adding more liquid if necessary. Serve with boiled new potatoes and vegetables in season.

SERVES 4 TO 6

Veal Makeover

To modify this recipe to a healthier version, reducing fat, kilojoules and cholesterol:

Meat is trimmed of all excess fat. The amount of meat is also reduced.

Polyunsaturated margarine is used in place of butter and the amount used is halved.

Egg yolks have been removed.

Cream (optional) has been replaced with reduced cream.

No salt is used.

VEAL IN CREAM SAUCE

If extra thickening is required, blend 1 tablespoon cornflour (cornstarch) with a little water. Blend into sauce. Cook, stirring until boiling and thickened.

- 750 g (1½ lb) veal shoulder, trimmed, boned and cubed
- 2 carrots, quartered lengthways
- 1 onion, studded with 2 cloves
- 1 leek, sliced
- 2 cloves garlic
- 1 bouquet garni
- 60 g (2 oz) polyunsaturated margarine
- 500 g (1 lb) pickling onions
- 250 g (8 oz) button mushrooms
- 2 tablespoons plain (all-purpose) flour
- ½ cup (125 ml/4 fl oz) reduced cream (optional)
- pinch nutmeg
- seasonings, to taste

Place veal in a large saucepan. Cover with water. Bring to the boil. Drain well. Rinse pan to remove any scum. Return veal to saucepan.

Add carrots, onion, leek, garlic and bouquet garni. Cover with water. Bring to the boil. Reduce heat. Simmer, covered, for 1¼ hours.

Melt margarine in a large frying pan. Sauté onions and mushrooms until onions are golden and tender. Remove from pan.

Remove veal and carrots from stock. Strain stock, discarding vegetables. Blend flour into remaining margarine in frying pan. Cook, stirring, for 1 minute. Remove from heat.

Gradually blend 3½ cups (875 ml/1½ pt) of reserved stock into roux (margarine and flour mixture). Return to heat. Cook, stirring constantly, until sauce boils and thickens. Simmer for 3 minutes.

Add meat, carrots, onions and mushrooms to sauce. Blend in cream. Reheat gently. Serve with noodles, rice and vegetables.

SERVES 4 TO 6

BRAISED VEAL IN MUSHROOM SAUCE

- 90 g (3 oz) butter or margarine
- 1¼ kg/2½ lb boned leg or shoulder of veal
- 2 onions, chopped
- 2 spring onions, chopped
- 1¾ cups (440 ml/14 fl oz) apple cider
- 1 sprig thyme
- 1 bay leaf
- seasonings, to taste
- 250 g (8 oz) mushrooms, sliced
- ½ cups (125 ml/4 oz) cream
- 1 egg yolk
- 2 tablespoons chopped fresh parsley

Melt three-quarters of butter in a large frying pan. Cook veal gently until browned on all sides. Transfer to a plate.

Sauté onions and spring onions in same pan. Return meat to pan with cider, herbs and seasonings. Bring to the boil. Reduce heat. Simmer for 1½ hours.

Melt remaining butter in a small pan. Sauté mushrooms for 3 minutes. Stir into veal. Simmer for a further 10 minutes.

Place drained veal on a serving platter. Discard thyme and bay leaf from sauce. Whisk in combined cream and egg yolk until thickened. Pour over meat. Sprinkle with parsley. Serve with salad and crusty bread.

SERVES 4 TO 6

COOKING WITH VEAL

When cooking veal in casseroles, stews, hotpots and soups, don't use expensive cuts – ask your butcher for advice.

VEAL IN WINE

....

1kg (2 lb) boned shoulder of veal, cubed

½ cup (60 g/2 oz) plain flour

30 g (1 oz) butter or margarine

2 tablespoons oil

2 large onions, finely chopped

2 cloves garlic, crushed

2 cups (500 ml/16 fl oz) chicken stock

1¼ cups (315 ml/10 fl oz) dry white wine

1 tablespoon tomato paste

1 bouquet garni

seasonings, to taste

16 pickling onions

250 g (8 oz) button mushrooms, sliced

2 tomatoes, peeled and chopped

1 teaspoon sugar

4 slices white bread

1 tablespoon butter or margarine, extra

2 tablespoons chopped fresh parsley

Preheat oven to 180°C (350°F).

Dust veal in half of the flour. Shake off excess. Heat half of the butter and oil in a large frying pan. Brown meat well. Transfer to a casserole dish.

Heat remaining butter and oil in pan. Sauté the onions and garlic until tender. Sprinkle in the remaining flour. Cook, stirring, until golden.

Remove pan from heat. Gradually blend in stock and wine. Return to heat. Cook, stirring constantly, until sauce boils and thickens.

Blend in tomato paste, bouquet garni and seasonings. Simmer gently until liquid is reduced by half. Pour over meat, add onions.

Bake for 1 hour or until meat is tender. Stir in mushrooms, tomatoes and sugar. Bake for a further 15 minutes.

Slice bread into quarters diagonally. Heat extra butter in a small pan. Fry bread until crisp and golden (croutons).

Dip each crouton into the meat sauce and then the parsley. Garnish casserole with croutons. Serve with salad.

SERVES 6

Poultry and Game

*O*nce a meat reserved for special occasions, chicken is now inexpensive and widely available in a variety of interesting 'cuts'. Game birds and rabbit have full give dishes a distinctive flavour. They are readily available at specialist poultry shops and some delicatessens, although it is often a good idea to order ahead.

CHICKEN, CARROT AND ORANGE SOUP

6 carrots, sliced

2 stalks celery, sliced

1 onion, sliced

4 cups (1 litre/32 fl oz) chicken stock

1 bay leaf

seasonings, to taste

1 tablespoon cornflour (cornstarch)

rind and juice 1 orange

pinch nutmeg

¼ cup (60 ml/2 fl oz) cream

Place carrots, celery and onion in a large saucepan with 1 ½ cups (375 ml/12 fl oz) stock, bay leaf and seasonings. Simmer for 30 minutes. Remove bay leaf.

Process vegetables and stock in a food processor or blender until smooth. Return to saucepan.

Blend cornflour with a little of the remaining stock to form a smooth paste. Blend into vegetable purée with remaining stock, orange rind and juice and nutmeg.

Chicken, Carrot and Orange Soup

Heat, stirring constantly, until soup boils and thickens. Simmer for 3 minutes. Serve garnished with a swirl of cream.

SERVES 4 TO 6

TURKISH CHICKEN SOUP WITH YOGHURT

Chopped, cooked chicken may be added to soup with the yoghurt.

- *8 cups (2 litres/70 fl oz) chicken stock*
- *¼ cup (45 g/1½ oz) rice*
- *seasonings, to taste*
- *1 cup (250 ml/8 fl oz) natural yoghurt*
- *2 egg yolks, lightly beaten*
- *2 tablespoons chopped fresh parsley*
- *1 tablespoon chopped fresh mint*

Bring chicken stock to the boil in a large saucepan. Add rice and seasonings. Simmer for 20 minutes.

Blend yoghurt into egg yolks. Add a little hot stock to yoghurt mixture. Beat until smooth.

Whisk yoghurt mixture into hot stock. Heat gently, but do not boil. Sprinkle with parsley and mint. Serve with pitta bread.

SERVES 4 TO 6

SPICY CHICKEN AND AVOCADO SOUP

- *1 chicken breast*
- *8 cups (2 litres/70 fl oz) chicken stock*
- *2 onions, thinly sliced*
- *1 teaspoon curry powder*
- *½ teaspoon ground coriander*
- *½ teaspoon ground oregano*
- *seasonings, to taste*
- *1 avocado, peeled, seeded and sliced*

Place chicken in a large saucepan with stock, onions, curry powder, herbs and seasonings. Bring to the boil. Reduce heat. Simmer for 20 minutes.

Remove chicken from stock. Cool, then strain stock, discarding onion. Return stock to saucepan with sliced chicken breast. Reheat gently.

Spicy Chicken and Avocado Soup

Place avocado slices in serving bowls. Pour over soup. Serve with crusty bread.

SERVES 4 TO 6

AVOCADOES

If leaving sliced avocado exposed to air, brush lightly with lemon juice to help prevent discolouration.

FARMHOUSE CHICKEN AND POTATO CASSEROLE

4 to 6 chicken pieces

3 tablespoons plain (all-purpose) flour

60 g (1 oz) butter or margarine

1 tablespoon oil

500 g (1 lb) potatoes, peeled and cut into chunks

8 pickling onions, peeled

4 rashers (125 g/4 oz) rindless bacon, cut into strips

60 g (2 oz) mushrooms, sliced

¾ cup (185 ml/6 fl oz) chicken stock

1 tablespoon snipped chives

Preheat oven to 180°C (350°F).

Dust chicken pieces with flour, shaking off excess. Heat butter and oil together in a frying pan. Fry chicken pieces until golden on both sides. Drain well. Place in a casserole dish with potatoes.

Sauté onions, bacon and mushrooms in same pan until golden. Transfer to the casserole dish.

Pour stock into pan. Bring to the boil, stirring to incorporate pan juices. Pour into casserole.

Bake, covered, for 1 hour or until chicken is tender. Sprinkle with chives. Serve with vegetables of choice.

SERVES 4 TO 6

Farmhouse Chicken and Potato Casserole

CHICKEN IN PORT

1½ kg (3 lb) chicken, segmented

3 tablespoons seasoned flour

¼ cup (60 ml/2 fl oz) oil

4 rashers (125 g/4 oz) rindless bacon, chopped

1 onion, chopped

125 g (4 oz) button mushrooms, sliced

1 cup (250 ml/8 fl oz) port

seasonings, to taste

¾ cup (185 ml/6 fl oz) sour cream or natural yoghurt

½ teaspoon honey

Preheat oven to 180°C (350°F).

Dust chicken pieces in seasoned flour, shaking off excess. Heat oil in a large frying pan. Fry chicken for about 10 minutes, turning occasionally, until golden on all sides. Transfer to a casserole dish.

Sauté bacon and onion in same oil for about 2 minutes. Add mushrooms. Sauté for 1 minute more.

Stir in port and seasonings. Simmer for 5 minutes. Pour over chicken. Bake, covered, for 30 minutes or until chicken is tender.

Blend the sour cream and honey together. Stir into casserole. Return to oven for a further 10 minutes. Serve with salad and crusty bread.

SERVES 4 TO 6

CHICKEN WITH OLIVES AND FENNEL

If button mushrooms are unavailable, use large mushrooms, quartered.

30 g (1 oz) butter or margarine

4 rashers (125 g/4 oz) rindless bacon, cut into strips

4 to 6 chicken pieces

4 spring onions, chopped

1 onion, chopped

1 carrot, sliced

1 tablespoon plain (all-purpose) flour

1¼ cups (315 ml/10 fl oz) dry white wine

3 tablespoons tomato paste

¼ teaspoon fennel seeds

seasonings, to taste

15 g (½ oz) butter or margarine, extra

250 g (8 oz) button mushrooms

125 g (4 oz) pitted green olives

Melt butter in a large pan. Sauté bacon until golden. Remove with a slotted spoon. Drain on kitchen paper.

Fry chicken pieces in same pan until golden on all sides. Drain well.

Sauté spring onions, onion and carrot in same pan until tender. Stir in the

Chicken with Olives and Fennel

flour. Cook for 1 minute. Remove from heat.

Gradually blend in combined wine and tomato paste. Return to heat. Cook, stirring constantly, until mixture boils and thickens.

Stir in fennel and seasonings. Simmer for 3 minutes. Return chicken to pan. Simmer, covered, for 30 minutes or until chicken is tender.

Melt extra butter in a small frying pan. Sauté mushrooms for 3 to 4 minutes. Add to casserole with bacon and olives. Simmer for a further 10 minutes. Serve with boiled new potatoes and vegetables in season.

SERVES 4 TO 6

CHICKEN TARRAGON

- 1½ kg (3 lb) chicken
- 15 g (½ oz) butter or margarine
- 1 teaspoon dried tarragon
- seasonings, to taste
- 30 g (1 oz) butter or margarine, extra
- 2 carrots, diced
- 1 onion, finely chopped
- ½ cup (125 ml/4 fl oz) chicken stock
- ½ teaspoon dried tarragon, extra
- 1 tablespoon cornflour
- 2 tablespoons water

Preheat oven to 180°C (350°F).

Thoroughly wash and dry inside and outside of chicken. Place butter, tarragon and seasonings in cavity. Truss the chicken.

Heat extra butter in a large frying pan. Brown the chicken on all sides. Transfer to a plate.

Sauté carrots and onion in same pan until tender. Place in the base of a casserole dish. Place chicken on top.

Add stock and extra tarragon. Cover tightly with foil. Bake for 1 hour or until chicken is cooked and tender.

Cut the chicken into serving pieces. Keep warm. Blend cornflour with water to form a smooth paste. Blend into pan juices with vegetables. Cook, stirring constantly until sauce boils and thickens. Simmer for 3 minutes. Pour over chicken. Serve with vegetables of choice.

SERVES 4 TO 6

LOW FAT CHICKEN

Remove skin from chicken pieces to reduce fat, cholesterol and kilojoules. Skin is easily removed from chicken pieces. Simply ease fingertips under skin and pull.

AROMATIC CHICKEN AND VEGETABLE STEW

- 1½ kg (3 lb) chicken pieces
- ½ teaspoon paprika
- ¼ teaspoon ground marjoram
- salt and freshly ground black pepper, to taste
- 60 g (2 oz) butter or margarine
- 2 tablespoons oil
- 2 onions, sliced
- 2 carrots, sliced
- 1 leek, sliced
- 425 g (13½ oz) canned butter beans, drained
- 1¼ cups (315 ml/10 fl oz) chicken stock
- 1 teaspoon fresh lemon juice

Thoroughly dry chicken with kitchen paper. Rub with combined paprika, marjoram and seasonings.

Heat half of the butter and oil in a large, heavy-based pan. Brown chicken well on all sides. Drain on kitchen paper.

Heat remaining butter and oil in same pan. Sauté onions until golden. Add carrots, leek and beans. Cook gently for 10 to 15 minutes.

Return chicken to pan with stock. Simmer, covered, for about 1 hour or until chicken is cooked and tender.

Stir in lemon juice. Serve with jacket potatoes and vegetables of choice.

SERVES 4 TO 6

BAKED CHICKEN WITH TOMATOES

- 1¼ kg (2½ lb) chicken pieces
- ½ cup (60 g/2 oz) seasoned flour
- 60 g (2 oz) butter or margarine
- 2 tablespoons oil
- 60 g (2 oz) butter or margarine, extra
- 3 spring onions, chopped
- 250 g (8 oz) button mushrooms, sliced
- 425 g (13½ oz) canned tomatoes, chopped
- 1 cup (250 ml/8 fl oz) dry white wine
- ¾ cup (185 ml/6 fl oz) chicken stock
- 1 sprig tarragon
- seasoning, to taste

Preheat oven to 180°C (350°F).

Dust chicken in seasoned flour, shaking off excess. Heat butter and oil together in a frying pan. Brown chicken well on all sides. Transfer to a casserole dish.

Melt extra butter in same pan. Sauté spring onions until tender. Add mushrooms. Sauté for 2 to 3 minutes.

Add all remaining ingredients. Bring to the boil. Pour over chicken.

Bake, covered, for 1 hour or until chicken is tender. Serve with rice and salad.

SERVES 4 TO 6

SEGMENTING CHICKEN

Segment a chicken into 8 serving pieces by removing leg and thigh at joint and halving through thigh joint; removing wing and part of breast and then chopping breast from carcass and halving through the breast bone. If you prefer, purchase pieces.

APRICOT CHICKEN

Duck or other poultry may be used with peaches or apricots.

2 cloves garlic

½ teaspoon ground ginger

¼ teaspoon chilli powder

¼ teaspoon saffron

1 tablespoon hot milk

1 tablespoon oil

2 onions, finely chopped

1½ kg (3 lb) chicken pieces

2 tomatoes, chopped

¼ teaspoon garam masala

seasonings, to taste

3 cups (750 ml/3 pt 5 fl oz) chicken stock or water

250 g (8 oz) apricots, peeled and stoned

Pound garlic into a paste with ginger and chilli. Crumble saffron into milk. Allow to dissolve.

Heat oil in a large saucepan. Sauté onions until golden. Stir in garlic paste. Cook gently, stirring, for about 5 minutes.

Add the chicken, tomatoes, garam masala and seasonings to pan. Pour over stock. Simmer, covered, for about 1 hour or until chicken is cooked. Add more stock as required.

Stir in apricots and saffron. Simmer gently until apricots are tender. Serve with rice.

SERVES 4 TO 6

Apricot Chicken

ALTERNATIVE TO FRESH APRICOTS

A 425 g (13½ oz) can apricot halves, drained, or 125 g (4 oz) dried apricots soaked in water overnight, may be used in place of fresh apricots.

PEELING STONED FRUIT

Peel stone fruit by plunging in boiling water for 30 seconds to 1 minute. Drain. Skin will peel away easily. To remove stones, cut around centre, twist and pull halves apart and remove stone.

CREAMY TURKEY WITH MUSHROOMS

- *90 g (3 oz) butter or margarine*
- *4 leeks, sliced*
- *2 onions, sliced*
- *2 carrots, sliced*
- *1 stalk celery, sliced*
- *4 rashers (125 g/4 oz) rindless bacon, cut into strips*
- *1 bouquet garni*
- *seasonings, to taste*
- *4 to 6 turkey portions*
- *1 cup (250 ml/8 fl oz) chicken stock*
- *250 g/8 oz button mushrooms*
- *juice 2 lemons*
- *4 potatoes, peeled and cut into chunks*
- *½ cup (125 ml/4 fl oz) cream*
- *1 egg yolk*

Melt 30 g (1 oz) butter in a large flameproof casserole dish. Sauté vegetables, bacon, bouquet garni and seasonings until bacon is golden.

Add turkey and stock. Simmer, covered, for about 1 hour. Add more stock if required.

Melt remaining butter in frying pan. Sauté mushrooms for 3 to 4 minutes. Stir in half of the lemon juice. Set aside.

Add potatoes to casserole. Cook for a further 30 minutes. Arrange turkey and potatoes on a serving platter. Keep warm.

Whisk the cream into the egg yolk with the remaining lemon juice. Blend into the sauce with the mushrooms.

Heat gently, stirring constantly, until sauce begins to thicken. Pour sauce over turkey and potatoes. Serve with salad.

SERVES 4 TO 6

PHEASANT WITH RED WINE SAUCE

- *1¼ kg (2½ lb) pheasant*
- *3 tablespoons seasoned flour*
- *60 ml (2 fl oz) oil*
- *1 onion, sliced*
- *1 red capsicum (pepper), seeded and diced*
- *1 green capsicum (pepper), seeded and diced*
- *60 g (2 oz) mushrooms, sliced*
- *½ cup (125 ml/4 fl oz) red wine*
- *1¼ cups (315 ml/10 fl oz) chicken stock*
- *1 tablespoon tomato paste*
- *pinch ground mace*
- *seasonings, to taste*
- *1 tablespoon cornflour*
- *¼ cup (60 ml/2 oz) water*

Preheat oven to 180°C (350°F).

Cut pheasant into 6 portions (drumsticks, thighs and breasts). Dust in seasoned flour, shaking off excess.

Heat oil in a frying pan. Brown pheasant well. Transfer to a casserole dish. Sauté onion in same oil until tender. Add capsicum and mushrooms. Sauté for 2 to 3 minutes. Pour in wine. Simmer for 5 minutes.

Stir in stock, tomato paste, mace and seasonings. Blend cornflour with water to form a smooth paste. Gradually whisk into sauce, stirring constantly, until sauce boils and thickens.

Pour over the pheasant. Bake, covered, for 45 to 60 minutes or until tender. Serve with creamed potatoes and vegetables in season.

SERVES 4 TO 6

BAKED DUCK WITH TAGLIATELLE

- *60 g (2 oz) butter or margarine*
- *2 x 1½ kg (3 lb) ducks, quartered*
- *60 ml (2 fl oz) oil*
- *2 onions, chopped*
- *2 carrots, sliced*
- *2 stalks celery, chopped*
- *1 kg (2 lb) tomatoes, peeled and chopped or 850 g (1 lb 11 oz) canned tomatoes, chopped*
- *125 g (4 oz) bacon pieces, or chopped bacon*
- *1¼ cups (315 ml/10 fl oz) chicken stock*
- *1½ cups (125 ml/4 fl oz) dry white wine*
- *1 teaspoon chopped fresh parsley*
- *¼ teaspoon each dried basil and sage*
- *seasonings, to taste*
- *2 teaspoons cornflour (cornstarch)*
- *375 g (12 oz) tagliatelle*
- *⅓ cup (45 g/1½ oz) grated Parmesan cheese*

Preheat oven to 180°C (350°F).

Heat half of butter and all the oil in a large frying pan. Brown duck pieces well on all sides. Drain well. Transfer to a casserole dish.

Sauté onions in same pan until tender. Add carrots and celery. Sauté for 5 minutes or until lightly browned. Transfer to casserole dish using a slotted spoon.

Add tomatoes, bacon, stock, wine, herbs and seasonings to casserole. Bake, covered, for 1 to 1¼ hours or until duck is tender. Transfer duck to a plate. Keep warm.

Strain the casserole liquid into a clean pan. Blend cornflour with a little of the juices to form a smooth paste. Whisk into juices. Bring to the boil, stirring constantly, until sauce boils and thickens.

Cook pasta in plenty of boiling water until tender. Drain well. Return to pan. Toss through remaining butter and cheese. Place on a serving platter. Arrange duck on top. Pour sauce over duck and pasta.

SERVES 6 TO 8

BAKED CHICKEN IN ORANGE SAUCE

1½ kg (3 lb) chicken pieces

3 tablespoons seasoned flour

30 g (1 oz) butter or margarine

2 tablespoons oil

1 onion, thickly sliced

1½ tablespoons plain (all-purpose) flour

2 cups (500 ml/16 fl oz) chicken stock

½ cup (125 ml/4 fl oz) dry white wine

juice and thinly sliced rind of 1 orange

1 tablespoon Worcestershire sauce

⅓ cup (60 g/2 oz) sultanas

seasonings, to taste

Preheat oven to 180°C (350°F).

Dust chicken in seasoned flour, shaking off excess. Heat butter and oil in a large frying pan. Brown chicken well on all sides. Transfer to a casserole dish.

Sauté onion in same pan until tender. Place in casserole.

Sprinkle flour into pan. Cook, stirring, for 1 minute. Remove from heat. Gradually blend in combined stock, wine, orange juice and Worcestershire sauce.

Baked Chicken in Orange Sauce

Return to heat. Cook, stirring constantly, until sauce boils and thickens. Simmer for 3 minutes. Stir in sultanas, orange rind and seasonings.

Pour sauce over chicken. Bake for about 1 hour or until chicken is cooked and tender. Serve with rice and salad.

SERVES 4 TO 6

ORANGE RIND

Peel the rind from the orange very thinly using a vegetable peeler, taking care to remove any white pith — this is very bitter. Cut into thin strips. Use as directed.

QUAIL IN MADEIRA

Quail are available from poultry stores. In some cases it is a good idea to order them ahead of time, to be sure they are available.

> 8 quail
>
> 3 tablespoons seasoned flour
>
> 125 g (4 oz) butter or margarine
>
> 250 g (8 oz) mushrooms, sliced
>
> 440 g (14 oz) canned chicken consommé
>
> 1 cup (250 ml/8 oz) Madeira
>
> 2 stalks celery, sliced
>
> 1 lemon, thinly sliced
>
> 1 tablespoon chopped fresh parsley
>
> croutons to serve

Preheat oven to 180°C (350°F).

Dust each bird lightly in seasoned flour, shaking off excess. Melt butter in a large frying pan. Brown quail well. Transfer to a casserole dish.

Sauté mushrooms in same pan for 2 to 3 minutes. Stir in consomme and Madeira. Bring to the boil. Pour over quail. Top with celery, lemon and parsley. Bake, covered, for 1 hour or until tender.

Discard celery and lemon before serving. Place each quail on a rectangular crouton. Mask with sauce. Serve with boiled new potatoes and vegetables in season.

SERVES 4 TO 6

MASK

'Mask' is a cookery term, meaning to lightly coat the food with sauce — the food must not 'swim' in sauce.

RABBIT WITH MUSTARD SAUCE

Chicken may be used in place of rabbit.

> 1 rabbit
>
> 60 g (2 oz) French mustard
>
> salt and freshly ground black pepper, to taste
>
> 6 rashers (185 g/6 oz) rindless bacon
>
> ½ cup (125 ml/4 fl oz) cream

Preheat oven to 180°C (350°F).

Wash and dry rabbit thoroughly inside and out. Spread half the mustard in cavity. Sprinkle the outside with seasonings.

Chicken with Wine and Herbs

Place rabbit in a casserole dish just large enough to hold it. Cover the rabbit with bacon slices. Spread the remaining mustard over this.

Bake, covered, for 1 to 1½ hours or until tender.

Transfer rabbit to a serving platter. Keep warm. Pour cooking juices into a saucepan. Add cream. Bring to the boil. Simmer until sauce begins to thicken. Serve rabbit in segments with sauce and a salad.

SERVES 4 TO 6

Chicken Makeover

*T*o modify this recipe to a healthier version, reducing fat, kilojoules and cholesterol:

Skin is removed from chicken.

Seasoned flour is omitted.

No butter is used. Instead olive oil or polyunsaturated margarine is used.

Ham is used in place of bacon.

No salt is used.

CHICKEN WITH WINE AND HERBS

2 tablespoons olive oil

125 g (4 oz) ham, sliced

12 pickling onions

2 carrots, sliced

1 clove garlic, crushed

30 g (1 oz) polyunsaturated margarine

2 kg (4 lb) chicken pieces, skin removed

½ cup (125 ml/4 fl oz) brandy

2 tomatoes, peeled, seeded and chopped

1½ cups (375 ml/12 fl oz) red wine

1 tablespoon chopped fresh parsley

1 bay leaf

½ teaspoon dried thyme

freshly ground black pepper, to taste

250 g (8 oz) button mushrooms

Heat oil in a large, heavy-based saucepan. Cook ham until lightly browned. Add onions, carrots and garlic. Cook, stirring, until onions are golden. Remove from pan. Drain on crumpled kitchen paper. Set aside.

Melt margarine in same pan. Brown chicken pieces well. Warm brandy in a small saucepan. Ignite with a long taper. Pour over chicken.

When flames subside, return ham mixture to pan with tomatoes. Cook for a few minutes.

Blend in wine, parsley, bay leaf, thyme and pepper. Simmer, covered, for 45 minutes. Add mushrooms to casserole. Simmer for a further 15 minutes or until chicken is tender. Serve with pasta and salad.

SERVES 4 TO 6

RABBIT IN BRANDY

1 rabbit, jointed

3 tablespoons seasoned flour

60 g (2 oz) butter or margarine

4 rashers (125 g/4 oz) rindless bacon, chopped

2 onions, chopped

3 tablespoons brandy

24 pickling onions

250 g (8 oz) button mushrooms

1¾ cups (440 ml/14 fl oz) dry white wine

2 cloves garlic, crushed

1 teaspoon sugar

1 bouquet garni

1 sprig parsley

¼ teaspoon each dried tarragon and chervil

seasonings, to taste

½ cup (125 ml/4 fl oz) thickened cream

1 teaspoon Dijon mustard

1 tablespoon chopped fresh parsley

Dust rabbit in seasoned flour, shaking off excess. Heat butter in a large, heavy-based saucepan. Brown rabbit well on all sides. Cook for about 10 minutes.

Add bacon. Cook for 2 minutes. Add chopped onions. Cook for 2 minutes more.

Warm the brandy in a small saucepan. Ignite with a long taper. Pour over rabbit.

When flame has subsided, add pickling onions, mushrooms, wine, garlic, sugar, bouquet garni, herbs and seasonings. Bring to the boil. Reduce heat. Simmer, covered, for 40 minutes.

Whisk cream with mustard and about 5 tablespoons of cooking liquid. Blend into casserole. Heat through gently. Sprinkle with parsley. Serve with boiled new potatoes and a green salad.

SERVES 4 TO 6

Napkins and jug from Home & Garden on the Mall, Skygarden, Sydney

Fish

*F*ish can be a great change from red meat or chicken in casseroles, stews and soups. This chapter features some wonderful ideas to transform a piece of fish into a hearty main meal, which is also nutritious.

FISH AND VEGETABLE BAKE

- 250 g (8 oz) fresh or frozen cod fillets
- 6 potatoes, sliced
- 3 onions, cut into wedges
- 6 tomatoes, seeded and cut into quarters
- 2 red capsicum (peppers), seeded and cut into strips
- 1 cucumber, peeled and cut into thick chunks
- 1 clove garlic, crushed
- 1 teaspoon salt
- freshly ground black pepper
- ½ cup (125 ml/4 fl oz) oil

Preheat oven to 190°C (375°F).

If using fresh fish, place in a little cold water and poach gently. Frozen cod should be thawed first.

Cut fish fillets across in thick slices. Layer fish and vegetables in an ovenproof casserole. Add garlic and pepper. Pour oil over. Cover with a lid and bake for about 45 minutes or until the vegetables are cooked. Serve straight from the casserole.

SERVES 4

SEAFOOD IN FRESH TOMATO SAUCE

- 300 g (10 oz) uncooked prawns (shrimps), shelled and deveined
- 125 g (4 oz) seafood sticks
- 125 g (4 oz) thick fish fillet
- 125 g (4 oz) scallops
- flour, seasoned with salt and pepper
- 2 tablespoons oil
- 1 clove garlic, chopped
- 250 g (8 oz) ripe tomatoes, peeled and chopped
- 1½ tablespoons white wine
- salt and freshly ground black pepper, to taste
- 2 tablespoons chopped fresh parsley

FRESH TOMATO SAUCE

- 500 g (1 lb) tomatoes, peeled and chopped
- ½ cup (125 ml/4 fl oz) white vinegar
- ½ cup (125 g/4 oz) sugar
- 1 tablespoon salt
- 1 tablespoon black peppercorns
- 1 tablespoon whole allspice
- 1 tablespoon crushed cinnamon stick
- ½ tablespoon mustard seeds
- ½ tablespoon whole cloves
- ¼ teaspoon cayenne pepper

Cut prawns, seafood sticks and fish fillets into 2½ cm (1 in) lengths. Coat all seafood in seasoned flour, shaking off any excess. Heat oil in a frying pan until hot, then add seafood. Fry until light golden colour, turning frequently, then drain the seafood on absorbent paper.

To Prepare Fresh Tomato Sauce: Put tomatoes into a saucepan and cook gently until reduced to a pulp. Rub through a colander to remove seeds.

Cook strained pulp, vinegar and sugar gently for 2 hours or until thick, then season with salt. Tie spices in a piece of muslin cloth and drop into the mixture. Gently boil sauce, stirring occasionally, until it reaches desired consistency.

Sauté garlic gently in frying pan for 1 minute. Stir into Tomato Sauce, add tomatoes and cook for 10 minutes more. Stir in wine and simmer until

Picture previous pages: Cod Simmered with Tomatoes (page 70), Seafood Baked with Artichokes (page 71)

reduced by half. Season to taste with salt and pepper. Add parsley and mix in seafood. Serve with rice.

SERVES 4

TO MAKE CROUTONS

Make croutons by frying quarters of crustless bread in 60 g (2 oz) butter and 2 tablespoons oil. Drain on crumpled kitchen paper. Try dipping the ends in chopped parsley.

FISHERMAN'S STEW

- 2 kg (4 lb) whole fish, scaled and gutted (whiting, bream, flathead, leatherjacket)
- 3 spring onions, sliced
- 2 stalks celery, sliced
- 1 onion, finely chopped
- 1 leek, sliced (use only the white part)
- 1 bouquet garni
- seasonings, to taste
- 4 cups (1 litre/32 fl oz) red or white wine
- 90 g (3 oz) butter or margarine
- 4 rashers (125 g/4 oz) rindless bacon, diced
- 250 g (8 oz) button mushrooms
- 12 pickling onions
- 3 tablespoons plain (all-purpose) flour
- croutons

Cut fish across the bone into thick steaks. Place in a large saucepan with spring onions, celery, onion, leek, bouquet garni and seasonings.

Pour over wine. Bring to the boil. Reduce heat. Simmer for 15 to 20 minutes. Transfer fish to a plate. Strain and reserve liquid.

Melt 30 g (1 oz) butter in the same pan. Sauté bacon until golden. Add mushrooms and onions. Sauté for 3 minutes or until onions are golden. Transfer mixture to plate with fish.

Melt remaining butter in same pan. Add flour. Cook, stirring, until flour is golden. Remove from heat. Gradually blend in reserved liquid. Return to heat. Cook, stirring constantly, until sauce boils and thickens. Simmer for 3 minutes.

Return fish, bacon, mushrooms and onions to pan. Heat gently to warm through. Garnish with croutons. Serve with boiled new potatoes and salad.

SERVES 4 TO 6

COOKING SEAFOOD

Never overcook fish or shellfish as it will become tough. As a general rule, cook fish until it flakes easily when tested with a fork. Shellfish is cooked when it changes colour. This usually only takes a matter of a few minutes. For this reason, add fish and shellfish at the end of the cooking time, unless otherwise directed.

TOMATO AND SMOKED HERRING SOUP

30 g (1 oz) butter or margarine

750 g (1½ lb) tomatoes, peeled and chopped

2 smoked herring fillets, chopped

1 clove garlic, crushed

2 tablespoons plain (all-purpose) flour

2 cups (500 ml/16 fl oz) milk

1¼ cups (315 ml/10 fl oz) water

seasonings, to taste

½ cup (125 ml/4 fl oz) cream

1 tablespoon sherry or fresh lemon juice

Melt butter in a saucepan. Stir in tomatoes, fish and garlic. Blend in flour. Cook, stirring, 1 minute. Remove from heat.

Gradually blend in milk and water. Return to heat. Cook, stirring constantly, until mixture boils and thickens. Stir in seasonings. Reduce heat. Simmer, covered, for 20 minutes.

Process in a food processor or blender until mixture is smooth — this may need to be done in several batches. Return mixture to saucepan.

Blend in cream and sherry. Reheat gently. Do not boil. Serve hot or cold with crusty bread.

SERVES 4 TO 6

FISH SOUP WITH FENNEL, ORANGE AND AÏOLI

1½ kg (3 lb) assorted fish

6 cups (1½ litres/48 fl oz) water

2 onions, chopped

3 cloves garlic, crushed

½ fennel bulb, chopped

2 bay leaves

1 teaspoon chopped fresh thyme

1 teaspoon chopped fresh parsley

grated rind of 1 orange

seasonings, to taste

5 egg yolks

croutes

AÏOLI

1 egg yolk

2 cloves garlic, crushed

1 cups (250 ml/8 fl oz) olive oil

fresh lemon juice

seasonings, to taste

Fillet fish, removing all skin, bones and heads. Cut flesh into 2 cm/¾ in pieces. Set aside.

Place fish head, bones and skin in a large saucepan with water, onions, garlic, fennel, bay leaves, thyme, parsley, rind and seasonings. Bring to the boil. Reduce heat. Simmer for 20 minutes.

Strain through 2 layers of damp muslin, pressing hard against bones.

Reheat liquid. Add fish pieces. Simmer for 3 minutes or until fish flakes easily when tested. Transfer fish to a soup tureen. Keep warm.

To Prepare Aïoli: Whisk egg yolk into garlic. Gradually whisk oil until thick. Flavour with lemon juice and seasonings.

Whisk aïoli with egg yolks. Whisk in a little of the hot soup. Whisk the egg yolk mixture into the soup. Heat gently, whisking, until thickened. Do not boil.

Pour soup over fish. Sprinkle with croutes. Serve with crusty bread.

SERVES 4 TO 6

PURCHASING FISH

Purchase fish the day it is to be used. Store in the refrigerator until required. Look for fish with bright eyes and gills and firm scales. They should also have a pleasant 'fishy' smell. Freeze any left over fresh fish or shellfish. Never refreeze thawed fish or shellfish.

BRANDY FISH STEW

60 g (2 oz) butter or margarine

3 tablespoons olive oil

1 rasher (30 g/1 oz) rindless
bacon, chopped

3 tablespoons plain (all-purpose)
flour

4 cups (1 litre/32 fl oz) water

2 cups (500 ml/16 fl oz) dry
white wine

2 tablespoons chopped fresh
parsley

1 clove garlic, crushed

1 bay leaf

¼ teaspoon ground thyme

pinch ground nutmeg

seasonings, to taste

1½ kg (3 lb) mixed, chopped fish
of choice

½ cup (125 ml/4 fl oz) brandy

toasted French bread

Heat butter and oil in a flameproof
casserole dish. Sauté bacon until
golden. Add flour. Cook, stirring,
until golden. Remove from heat.

Gradually blend in water and wine.
Return to heat. Cook, stirring
constantly, until sauce boils and
thickens. Add parsley, garlic, bay
leaf, thyme, nutmeg and seasonings.
Simmer, covered, for 20 minutes.

Stir in fish. Simmer, covered, for
10 minutes. Warm brandy. Ignite
with a long taper. Pour over
casserole. When flames subside, serve
in soup bowls, garnished with toast.

SERVES 4 TO 6

FISH STOCK

Prepare your own fish stock by covering
fish scraps with water. Add flavourings of
choice. Bring to the boil. Simmer for
20 minutes. Strain. Prepare the day it is
to be used. Do not freeze.

Brandy Fish Stew

MUSSEL AND PRAWN SOUP WITH WINE

4 cups (1 litres/32 fl oz) fish stock

250 g (8 oz) tomatoes, peeled,
seeded and chopped

½ cup (125 ml/4 fl oz) white wine

1 clove garlic, crushed

2 strips orange rind

2 sprigs parsley and fennel

sprig thyme

pinch saffron threads

750 g (1½ lb) fish fillets, sliced

375 g (12 oz) mussels, scrubbed
and beards removed

250 g (8 oz) green uncooked
prawns (shrimp), shelled and
deveined

4 to 6 green king prawns (large
shrimp), extra

oil for shallow frying

ROUILLE

1 green capsicum (pepper), seeded
and halved

1 fresh chilli, seeded and halved

250 g (8 oz) canned pimento,
drained

3 cloves garlic

1½ tablespoons oil

breadcrumbs

seasonings, to taste

Place stock, tomatoes, wine, garlic,
rind, parsley, fennel, thyme and
saffron in a large pan. Bring to the
boil. Reduce heat. Simmer for
20 minutes. Strain.

Reheat stock. Add fish, prawns and
mussels to pan. Simmer for 5 minutes.
Discard any mussels that do not open.

Fry extra prawns in a little oil until
they change colour. Top soup with a
spoonful of Rouille and a whole
prawn. Serve with crusty bread.

To Prepare Rouille: Place capsicum
and chilli in boiling water for
3 minutes. Drain well. Refresh
under cold running water.

Place pimento and garlic in a food
processor or blender. Process to a
paste. Add capsicum and chilli.
Process until smooth. Gradually add
oil and enough breadcrumbs to form
a firm mixture. Adjust seasonings.

SERVES 4 TO 6

Mussel and Prawn Soup with Wine

COD SIMMERED WITH TOMATOES

- 8 cod fillets (or other fillets of choice), cut into strips
- 2 tablespoons plain (all-purpose) flour, seasoned
- 2 tablespoons oil
- 1 onion, chopped
- 2 zucchini (courgettes), sliced
- 1 red capsicum (pepper), seeded and sliced
- 3 tomatoes, peeled and chopped
- 1 tablespoon tomato paste
- ½ cup (125 ml/4 fl oz) water
- ½ cup (125 ml/4 fl oz) sherry
- 1 tablespoon red wine vinegar
- 1 chicken stock cube, crumbled
- seasonings, to taste
- chopped fresh parsley

Wash and thoroughly dry fish. Sprinkle with flour. Set aside.

Heat oil in a flameproof casserole dish. Sauté onion until tender. Add zucchini and capsicum. Sauté for 3 minutes.

Stir in tomatoes and tomato paste. Cook, stirring, for 2 minutes. Blend in water, sherry, vinegar, stock cube and seasonings.

Bring to the boil. Reduce heat. Simmer, stirring occasionally, for 10 minutes.

Place fish in casserole. Simmer for 10 minutes. Sprinkle with parsley. Serve with boiled new potatoes and salad.

SERVES 4 TO 6

BAKED FISH FILLET GRATIN

- 30 g (1 oz) butter
- 2 tablespoons savoury biscuit crumbs
- 500 g (1lb) thick fish fillets, ling or gem fish
- 1 cup (250 g/8 oz) canned tomato pieces
- 1 onion, finely chopped
- salt and freshly ground black pepper, to taste
- ½ cup (60 g/2 oz) grated cheese

Preheat oven to 180°C (350°F).

Grease a shallow casserole dish with half the butter and sprinkle over the biscuit crumbs. Place fillets on crumbs.

Combine tomatoes, onion, salt and pepper and pour mixture over fish. Dot with remaining butter and sprinkle over cheese. Bake for 35 minutes or until fish flakes easily.

SERVES 2

BREAM AND MUSHROOM CASSEROLE

Obtain fish bones from your local fish shop or freeze any fish bones you may have to prepare stock when required. Fish stock should be used the day it is prepared.

STOCK

- 30 g (1 oz) butter or margarine
- 1 onion, chopped
- 250 g (8 oz) fish bones
- 2½ cups (625 ml/21 fl oz) dry white wine
- bouquet garni
- seasonings, to taste

CASSEROLE

- 2 spring onions, chopped
- 750 g (1½ lb) bream (or other white fish) fillets
- 250 g (8 oz) button mushrooms, sliced
- ½ cup (125 ml/4 fl oz) cream
- 1 egg yolk
- 1 teaspoon cornflour (cornstarch)
- juice ½ lemon
- 15 g (½ oz) butter or margarine
- 1 teaspoon chopped fresh parsley

Preheat oven to 180°C (350°F).

To Prepare Stock: Melt butter in a pan. Sauté onion until tender. Add remaining ingredients. Simmer for 5 minutes. Strain, reserving liquid. Set aside.

To Prepare Casserole: Sprinkle spring onions over the base of a casserole dish. Arrange fish on top. Top with half of the mushrooms and reserved stock. Bake, covered, for 20 minutes.

Transfer fish to a serving dish. Keep warm. Pour stock into a saucepan. Whisk in combined cream, egg yolk, cornflour and lemon juice. Heat gently.

Sauté remaining mushrooms in butter for 3 minutes. Toss through parsley. Pour sauce over fish. Garnish with mushrooms.

SERVES 4 TO 6

PRAWNS, MUSSELS AND SCALLOPS

Prawns should always be deveined to avoid grit. Always scrub mussels and remove beards. Scallops should have their digestive tract (the dark line on the scallop) removed with a sharp knife before using.

SEAFOOD BAKED WITH ARTICHOKES

If buying peeled, uncooked prawns, reduce the amount required to 300 g (9½ oz).

30 g (1 oz) butter or margarine

1 onion, chopped

500 g (1 lb) boneless fish fillets, cut into bite-sized pieces

250 g (8 oz) scallops, cleaned

250 g (8 oz) green uncooked prawns (shrimps), peeled and deveined

440 g (14 oz) canned mushroom soup

425 g (13½ oz) canned artichoke hearts, drained and halved

250 g (8 oz) mushrooms, sliced

1 cup (250 ml/8 fl oz) dry white wine

seasonings, to taste

2 cups (250 g/8 oz) cooked rice

2 teaspoons chopped fresh parsley

2 tablespoons grated Parmesan cheese

Preheat oven to 180°C (350°F).

Melt butter in a large frying pan. Sauté onion until tender. Stir in fish, scallops, prawns, soup, artichokes, mushrooms, wine and seasonings.

Combine rice and parsley. Spoon into a large greased casserole dish. Spoon over fish mixture. Bake for 20 minutes.

Sprinkle over cheese. Bake for a further 10 minutes. Serve with salad and crusty bread.

SERVES 4 TO 6

HEALTHY COOKING

Casseroles, stews, hotpots and soups make nutritious meals as the cooking liquid, containing nutrients from ingredients, is eaten as part of the dish.

PURCHASING FISH

If purchasing fish whole, they must be scaled and gutted before using. If you are unsure, ask your fishmonger to do it for you.

FISH CURRY WITH SAFFRON RICE

500 g (1 lb) fish fillets

¼ cup (60 ml/2 fl oz) water

¼ cup (60 ml/2 fl oz) milk

30 g (1 oz) butter or margarine

1 onion, finely chopped

2 tablespoons plain (all-purpose) flour

2 tablespoons curry powder

1 cup (250 ml/8 fl oz) dry white wine

water

200 g (6½ oz) shelled, cooked prawns (shrimp)

1 green capsicum (pepper), seeded and chopped

2 tablespoons sultanas

1 tablespoon desiccated coconut

1 tablespoon mango chutney

1 tablespoon fresh lemon juice

seasonings, to taste

SAFFRON RICE

60 ml (2 fl oz) oil

1 onion, chopped

1¼ cups (185 g/6 oz) long grain rice

4 cups (1 litre/32 fl oz) boiling water

1 chicken stock cube, crumbled

1 bay leaf

¼ teaspoon saffron or turmeric powder

½ cup (75 g/2½ oz) roasted peanuts

Preheat oven to 180°C (350°F).

Place fish in a saucepan with combined water and milk. Simmer for 2 minutes. Remove fish. Cut into bite-sized pieces. Reserve stock.

Melt butter in a frying pan. Sauté onion until tender. Stir in flour and curry powder. Cook, stirring, 1 minute.

Remove pan from heat. Make up the reserved fish stock to 2 cups (500 ml/16 fl oz) by adding wine and enough water. Gradually blend liquid into curry mixture. Return to heat. Cook, stirring constantly until sauce boils and thickens. Simmer for 3 minutes.

Stir in fish pieces, prawns, capsicum, sultanas, coconut, chutney, lemon juice and seasonings. Heat through gently. Serve with Saffron Rice.

To Prepare Saffron Rice: Heat oil in a frying pan. Sauté onion until tender. Add in rice. Cook, stirring, for 1 minute.

Pour the combined water, stock cube, bay leaf and saffron into pan with rice. Simmer, covered, for 5 minutes.

Transfer rice mixture to a shallow, oven-proof dish. Bake, covered, for 20 minutes. Serve, sprinkled with peanuts.

SERVES 4 TO 6

Remove seed from avocado, peel and cut into chunks.

Gradually blend sour cream into sauce; add chicken and crabmeat.

Pour into casserole and cover with crumbs.

CHICKEN, CRAB AND AVOCADO BAKE

- 2 avocados, peeled, seeded and cut into chunks
- 1 tablespoon fresh lemon juice
- 125 g (4 oz) butter or margarine
- 1 onion, chopped
- ½ cup (60 g/2 oz) plain (all-purpose) flour
- 1 teaspoon ground rosemary
- ¾ teaspoon paprika
- seasonings, to taste
- 3 cups (750 ml/25 fl oz) chicken stock
- ½ cup (125 ml/4 fl oz) sour cream
- 3 cups (375 g/12 oz) chopped cooked chicken
- 340 g (11 oz) canned crab meat, drained
- 1 cup (60 g/2 oz) buttered breadcrumbs

Preheat oven to 180°C (350°F).

Brush avocados with lemon juice. Set aside. Melt butter in a medium-sized saucepan. Sauté onion until tender. Blend in flour, rosemary, paprika and seasonings. Cook, stirring, for 1 minute.

Remove from heat. Gradually blend in stock. Return to heat. Cook, stirring constantly, until sauce boils and thickens. Blend in sour cream. Cook for 1 minute.

Blend in chicken, crab meat and avocado. Pour into a casserole dish. Sprinkle with crumbs. Bake for 30 minutes or until heated through and golden. Serve with salad.

SERVES 4 TO 6

Above: Chicken, Crab and Avocado Bake
Right: Haddock Risotto (recipe page 74)

BUTTERED BREADCRUMBS

Prepare buttered breadcrumbs, by sautéing fresh breadcrumbs in a little butter until completely coated.

HADDOCK RISSOTTO

60 ml (2 fl oz) oil

1 onion, chopped

1 clove garlic, crushed

1 green capsicum (pepper), seeded and chopped

125 g (4 oz) mushrooms, quartered

3 tomatoes, peeled and chopped

½ cup (90 g/3 oz) long grain rice

seasonings, to taste

1¼ cups (315 ml/10 fl oz) chicken stock

500 g (1 lb) smoked cod or haddock, cooked and flaked

30 g (1 oz) butter or margarine

juice ½ lemon

paprika

Heat oil in a large pan. Sauté onion and garlic until onion is tender. Add green capsicum. Sauté for 3 minutes.

Stir in mushrooms. Sauté for 1 minute. Blend in tomatoes, rice and seasonings. Cook, stirring, for about 3 minutes.

Pour in stock. Bring to the boil. Reduce heat. Simmer, covered, for about 20 minutes or until rice is tender. Add more stock if required, to prevent rice from sticking.

Poach smoked cod or haddock in enough water to cover for 3 to 5 minutes or until tender. Drain well.

Remove pan from heat. Stir in cod, butter and lemon juice. Dust with paprika. Serve immediately, with crusty bread.

SERVES 4 TO 6

MUSSELS

Mussel beards are the fuzzy growth protruding from the shell. This is easily removed by pulling with a knife.

TROUT IN RED WINE

90 g (3 oz) butter or margarine

4 to 6 trout, cleaned

1¼ cups (315 ml/10 fl oz) red wine

1 onion, chopped

1 clove garlic, crushed

1 bouquet garni

seasonings, to taste

2 tablespoons plain (all-purpose) flour

1 tablespoon tomato paste

pinch nutmeg

½ cup (125 ml/4 fl oz) sour cream

Preheat oven to 180°C (350°F).

Grease a large, shallow casserole dish with half of the butter. Arrange the fish side by side in the dish.

Pour over wine. Sprinkle with onion and garlic. Add bouquet garni and seasonings. Bake, covered, for 20 minutes.

Transfer fish to a plate. Remove skin from exposed side of fish, 4 cm (1½ in) below the head and 5 cm (2 in) above the tail, using a sharp knife. Keep warm. Strain stock from dish. Set aside.

Melt remaining butter in a small saucepan. Stir in flour, tomato paste and nutmeg. Cook 1 minute. Remove from heat.

Gradually blend in stock. Return to heat. Cook, stirring constantly, until sauce boils and thickens. Simmer for 3 minutes.

Blend in sour cream. Heat through gently. Pour sauce over trout. Serve with boiled new potatoes and salad.

SERVES 4 TO 6

SEAFOOD CURRY

2 tablespoons fresh lemon juice

250 g (8 oz) fish fillets, cut into bite-size pieces

250 g (8 oz) uncooked prawns (shrimps), peeled and deveined

125 g (4 oz) scallops

60 g (2 oz) calamari (squid) rings

2 tablespoons olive oil

60 g (2 oz) mussels in shell, cleaned

2 onions, chopped

1 teaspoon grated ginger

2 cloves garlic, crushed

½ teaspoon chilli powder

½ teaspoon cumin

¼ teaspoon garam masala

¼ teaspoon coriander

1 teaspoon turmeric

2 tomatoes, peeled and chopped

grated rind ½ lemon

½ cup (125 ml/4 fl oz) water

½ tablespoon chopped fresh parley

6 lemon twists, to garnish

Combine lemon juice, fish, prawns, scallops and calamari in a dish and set aside to marinate.

Heat olive oil in a large pan. Add mussels and cook over high heat for 5 to 7 minutes until shells open. Transfer mussels to a separate dish discarding any shells that have not opened. Set aside.

To the olive oil, add onions, ginger, garlic, spices, tomatoes, lemon rind and water. Bring to the boil, lower heat and simmer for 20 minutes. Add seafood marinade to pan and simmer for 10 minutes longer.

To serve, on individual plates spoon seafood curry onto a bed of boiled rice, then place mussels on side of plate. Sprinkle over parsley, and garnish with lemon twists.

SERVES 6

Fish Makeover

*T*o modify this recipe to a healthier version, reducing fat, kilojoules and cholesterol:

Tuna used is in brine not oil.

Butter is replaced with polyunsaturated margarine and amount halved.

Milk is replaced with stock.

Cheese used is low fat or low cholesterol variety and the amount used is also reduced.

No salt is used.

TUNA AND MACARONI BAKE WITH CHEESE

30 g (1 oz) polyunsaturated margarine

1 large onion, chopped

2 tablespoons plain (all-purpose) flour

1 tablespoon mustard powder

3 cups (750 ml/25 fl oz) chicken stock

½ cup (60 g/2 oz) grated low fat or low cholesterol cheese

1 tablespoon Worcestershire sauce

freshly ground black pepper, to taste

220 g (7 oz) canned tuna in brine, drained and flaked

1 cup (125 g/4 oz) macaroni, cooked

TOPPING

30 g (1 oz) low fat or low cholesterol cheese, cut into strips

2 tomatoes, sliced

freshly ground black pepper

Preheat oven to 180°C (350°F).

Melt margarine in a large frying pan. Sauté onion until tender. Add flour and mustard powder. Cook, stirring, for 1 minute. Remove from heat.

Blend in stock. Return to heat. Cook, stirring constantly, until sauce boils and thickens. Stir in cheese, sauce and seasonings. Simmer for 3 minutes.

Mix tuna and macaroni in sauce. Spoon into a casserole dish. Top with cheese, tomatoes and a sprinkling of pepper. Bake for 30 minutes. Serve with salad and crusty bread.

DILL AND SOUR CREAM FISH STEW

30 g (1 oz) butter or margarine

4 onions, sliced

1 potato, cubed

1 stalk celery, sliced

5 cups (1¼ litres/44 fl oz) milk

seasonings, to taste

1kg (2 lb) boneless fish fillets, cut into serving size pieces

½ cup (125 ml/4 fl oz) sour cream

2 tablespoons chopped dill pickle

1 tablespoon horseradish

1 tablespoon chopped fresh parsley

chopped fresh dill

Melt butter in a large saucepan. Sauté onions until tender. Add potato and celery. Sauté for 2 minutes.

Pour in milk and seasonings. Bring to the boil. Reduce heat. Simmer for 15 minutes. Add fish. Simmer for a further 5 minutes.

Stir in sour cream, pickle, horseradish and parsley. Heat through gently. Sprinkle with dill. Serve with crusty bread.

SERVES 4 TO 6

HORSERADISH

Horseradish belongs to the mustard family and it has a strong, sharp, burning flavour. The fresh, raw root is the most flavoursome part and adds a bite to sauces and dressings. You can buy jars of chopped horseradish at the supermarket, making it handy for use any time.

Vegetables

*J*ust about any vegetables can be used in casseroles, stews, hotpots and hearty soups. It depends on what you have available. Some of the recipes combine vegetables with meat – you can substitute this with tofu, more vegetables or pulses if you prefer.

WINTER VEGETABLE SOUP

90 g (3 oz) butter or margarine

2 onions, chopped

4 carrots, chopped

3 sticks celery, sliced

2 turnips, chopped

250 g (8 oz) jerusalem artichokes, peeled and cut into strips

125 g (4 oz) haricot beans, soaked in water overnight and drained

stock or water

1 bouquet garni

seasonings, to taste

½ cabbage, shredded

chopped fresh parsley

grated tasty cheese

Melt butter in a large saucepan. Sauté onions until tender. Add carrots, celery, turnips and artichokes. Cook, stirring, for 10 minutes.

Add the beans, enough stock to cover, bouquet garni and seasonings. Simmer, covered, for 1 hour.

Stir in cabbage. Simmer for a further 30 minutes. Sprinkle with parsley and cheese. Serve with crusty bread or rolls and a wedge of cheese.

SERVES 4 TO 6

DRIED BEANS

Dried beans can be soaked by a slow method or a quick method.

The slow method is to cover them with cold water and leave in a cold place overnight. Don't leave in a warm place or they will ferment.

The quick method is to boil them for 2 minutes, then remove from heat, cover and leave for 2 hours.

CAULIFLOWER CHEESE SOUP

1 small cauliflower, cut into florets

2 cups (500 ml/16 fl oz) vegetable stock or water

1 onion, sliced

1 bay leaf

30 g (1 oz) butter or margarine

1 tablespoon plain (all-purpose) flour

1 cup (250 ml/8 fl oz) milk

½ cup (60 g/2 oz) grated tasty cheese

seasonings, to taste

croutons

snipped chives

Simmer cauliflower, stock, onion and bay leaf for 20 minutes or until cauliflower is tender. Remove bay leaf.

Process cauliflower mixture in a food processor or blender until smooth. Set aside.

Melt butter in a large saucepan. Blend in flour. Cook 1 minute. Remove from heat.

Gradually blend in milk. Return to heat. Bring to the boil, stirring constantly until sauce boils and thickens. Simmer for 3 minutes.

Blend in purée, cream, cheese and seasonings. Heat through. Serve topped with croutons and snipped chives.

SERVES 4 TO 6

Picture previous pages: Artichokes with Lemon (page 85), Ratatouille (page 85).

HEARTY LENTIL SOUP

2 cups (400 g/12½ oz) green lentils

2½ cups (630 ml/21 fl oz) water

2 onions, chopped

2 cloves garlic, crushed

2 tablespoons olive oil

2 carrots, chopped

2 stalks celery, sliced

1 leek, washed and sliced

1 tablespoon paprika

3 cups (750 ml/25 fl oz) vegetable stock or water

¼ cup (60 ml/2 fl oz) dry red wine

¼ cup (60 ml/2 fl oz) red wine vinegar

1 bay leaf

seasonings, to taste

Soak lentils in water for 2 hours. Sauté onions and garlic in oil in a large pan until tender.

Add vegetables and paprika. Cook over a gentle heat until vegetables are tender.

Add undrained lentils, stock and remaining ingredients. Simmer, covered, for about 30 minutes or until lentils are tender. Serve with crusty bread.

SERVES 4 TO 6

PULSES (OR LEGUMES)

Pulses, which include dried beans and lentils, are an excellent substitute for meat. Not only are they cheaper and very filling, but they are rich sources of dietary fibre, complex carbohydrates, iron and various vitamins and minerals. Most of them are also very low in fat.

PUMPKIN SOUP

30 g (2 oz) butter or margarine

1 onion, finely chopped

500 g (1 lb) pumpkin, peeled and chopped

2½ cups (600 ml/20 fl oz) vegetable stock

pinch nutmeg

seasonings, to taste

½ cup (125 ml/4 fl oz) cream (optional)

1 tablespoon finely chopped fresh parsley or chives

Melt butter in a medium-sized saucepan. Sauté onion until tender. Add pumpkin. Cook, stirring, for 2 minutes.

Pour in stock. Simmer for 30 minutes or until pumpkin is tender. Purée mixture in a food processor or blender, adding nutmeg and seasonings.

Return soup to saucepan. Stir in cream. Heat gently. Sprinkle with parsley. Serve with rolls.

SERVES 4 TO 6

MUSHROOM SOUP WITH PARMESAN

30 g (1 oz) butter or margarine

1 tablespoon olive oil

1 onion, finely chopped

1 clove garlic, crushed

500 g (1 lb) mushrooms, thinly sliced

3 tablespoons tomato paste

3 cups (750 ml/25 fl oz) vegetable stock

2 tablespoons sweet vermouth

seasonings, to taste

4 egg yolks

3 tablespoons grated Parmesan cheese

2 tablespoons chopped fresh parsley

4 to 6 slices crusty bread, toasted and buttered

Heat butter and oil together in a large saucepan. Sauté onion and garlic until onion is tender. Add mushrooms. Cook for 5 minutes. Stir in tomato paste. Cook, stirring, 1 minute. Blend in stock, vermouth and seasonings. Simmer for 10 minutes.

Beat together egg yolks, cheese and parsley. Whisk into simmering soup. Serve immediately over bread.

SERVES 4 TO 6

LINGUINE AND TOMATO SOUP

2 tablespoons olive oil

⅓ cup (90 g 3 oz) chopped bacon

3 cloves garlic, crushed

½ cup (90 g/3 oz) chopped tomato

5 cups (1¼ litres/2 pt) stock or water

250 g (8 oz) linguine pasta, broken into pieces

freshly ground black pepper

¾ cup (90 g/3 oz) Parmesan cheese

1 teaspoon chopped fresh basil or ¼ teaspoon dried, to garnish

Heat oil in a pan and cook bacon and garlic until golden brown. Add tomato and stock, and bring to the boil.

Add linguine and cook for 15 minutes or until tender. Season to taste, then stir in half the cheese and basil. Sprinkle the remaining cheese over the soup and serve garnished with basil.

SERVES 4

VEGETABLE STOCK

Reserve your own vegetable stock from vegetable cooking water or use commercially prepared varieties.

TOMATO AND ROASTED CAPSICUM SOUP

1 red capsicum (pepper), cut in half

2 tablespoons oil

500 g (1 lb) ripe tomatoes, peeled and chopped

1 onion, chopped

1½ cups (375 ml/12 oz) vegetable stock

2 tablespoons tomato paste

cracked black pepper

shaved Parmesan cheese, to garnish

few sage leaves and rosemary fried in a litte oil

Place capsicum under hot grill or over gas flame and cook until skin blackens. When cool enough to handle remove skin and discard.

Heat oil in a pan, add tomatoes and onion and cook, stirring, over medium heat for 5 minutes.

Add capsicum, vegetable stock and tomato paste and cook over low heat for a further 15 minutes or until vegetables are soft. Place tomato mixture in bowl in food processor and process until puréed.

Return soup to saucepan, season with pepper and simmer until sauce is heated through. Ladle soup into bowls and garnish with Parmesan and fried herbs.

SERVES 4

CABBAGE BAKE

½ cabbage, shredded

250 g (8 oz) butter or margarine

seasonings, to taste

2 onions, sliced

2 green apples, peeled, cored and sliced

4 potatoes, peeled, parboiled and sliced

Preheat oven to 180°C (350°F).

Place a layer of cabbage in the base of a deep casserole dish. Dot with butter. Sprinkle with seasonings.

Top with layers of onion, apple and potato, dotting with butter and sprinkling with seasonings between each layer.

Repeat layers, finishing with a layer of potatoes. Dot with any remaining butter. Bake for 45 minutes or until potatoes are golden.

SERVES 4 TO 6

ONION SOUP

60 g (2 oz) butter or margarine

3 large onions, thinly sliced

1 tablespoon plain (all-purpose) flour

5 cups (1¼ litres/2 pt 4 fl oz) beef stock

seasonings, to taste

6 slices French bread stick

60 g (2 oz) tasty cheese, grated

olive oil

Melt butter in a large, heavy-based saucepan. Cook onions slowly, until golden brown and tender. Add flour. Cook, stirring for 1 minute. Remove from heat. Gradually blend in stock and seasonings.

Return to heat. Cook, stirring constantly, until boiling. Reduce heat. Simmer for 30 minutes.

To Prepare Cheese Croutes: Toast bread. Sprinkle cheese evenly over each slice of bread. Drizzle with a little olive oil. Grill until cheese melts and is golden.

Place cheese croutes in the base of individual soup dishes. Pour over soup. Serve immediately.

SERVES 4 TO 6

Onion Soup

Cabbage Bake

SIMMERED LENTILS, CAPSICUM (PEPPER) AND FENNEL

1 cup (200 g/6½ oz) green or brown lentils

4½ cups (1¼ litres/46 fl oz) vegetable stock or water

1 onion, chopped

2 cloves garlic, crushed

2 tablespoons olive oil

2 tomatoes, peeled and chopped

1 red capsicum (pepper), seeded and sliced

1 green capsicum (pepper), seeded and sliced

1 bulb fennel, trimmed and thinly sliced

1 stalk celery, sliced

¼ cup (60 ml/2 fl oz) cider vinegar

seasonings, to taste

chopped chives, fennel tops and parsley

Soak lentils in 1½ cups (375 ml/ 12 fl oz) stock for 2 hours. Sauté onion and garlic in oil in a large pan. Add vegetables. Cook, stirring occasionally, for 5 minutes.

Add undrained lentils, remaining stock, vinegar and seasonings. Bring to the boil.

Reduce heat. Simmer, covered, for 25 to 30 minutes or until lentils are tender. Serve sprinkled with herbs.

SERVES 4 TO 6

LENTILS

Brown and green lentils need to be cooked for 1-1½ hours, if not presoaked. Lentils are an excellent source of protein, fibre, vitamins and minerals. They are a good substitute for meat especially when minced meat is required.

LAYERED BEAN BAKE

1 onion, chopped

1 clove garlic, finely chopped

1 tablespoon olive oil

¼ cup chopped celery

1 tablespoon chilli sauce

½ cup tomato purée

¼ cup tomato paste

¼ cup red wine

½ teaspoon salt

¼ teaspoon freshly ground black pepper

¼ teaspoon dried oregano

¼ teaspoon dried basil

½ cup cooked butter beans

½ cup cooked chick peas

½ cup cooked red kidney beans

1 cup cooked soy beans

½ cup cooked lima beans

250 g (8 oz) Mozzarella cheese, sliced thinly

250 g (8 oz) ricotta cheese

grated Parmesan cheese

Preheat oven to 190°C (375°F).

Heat oil and cook onion, garlic and celery 5 minutes. Add chilli sauce, tomato purée and paste, wine, salt, pepper, oregano and basil. Simmer 25 minutes.

Combine all beans and peas in a bowl.

Beat ricotta cheese in a bowl until smooth. Place one-third tomato sauce in bottom of medium-sized casserole. Spoon in one-third bean mixture and spread one-third ricotta over beans. Place one-third Mozzarella cheese on ricotta. Repeat layers twice and sprinkle finished casserole with Parmesan.

Cover and bake for 30 minutes. Remove cover and bake 10 minutes more to brown.

SWEET POTATO CASSEROLE

4 large sweet potatoes, peeled

vegetable stock or water

60 g (2 oz) butter or margarine

220 g (7 oz) canned crushed pineapple, drained

2 tablespoons sweet sherry

½ teaspoon ground cinnamon

¼ teaspoon ground nutmeg

seasonings, to taste

Preheat oven to 180°C (350°F) .

Boil sweet potatoes in vegetable stock until tender. Drain well. Mash with butter.

Stir in all remaining ingredients. Spoon into a casserole dish. Bake for 15 minutes. Serve as a meal accompaniment.

SERVES 4 TO 6

LENTIL STEW

1 cup (200 g/6½ oz) brown lentils

1½ cups (375 ml/12 fl oz) vegetable stock or water

1 onion, chopped

3 cloves garlic, crushed

2 tablespoons oil

3 tomatoes, peeled and chopped

2 carrots, sliced

2 zucchini (courgettes), sliced

2 stalks celery, sliced

¼ cup (60 ml/2 fl oz) white wine vinegar

1 bay leaf

seasonings, to taste

500 g (1 lb) smoked sausage or ham, sliced (optional)

Soak lentils in stock for 2 hours. Sauté onion and garlic in oil in a large pan until tender.

Stir in undrained lentils, vegetables, bay leaf and seasonings. Bring to the boil. Add meat (optional).

Simmer, covered, for 45 minutes, adding more stock as required. Serve with salad and crusty bread.

SERVES 4 TO 6

POTATO AND SALAMI HOTPOT

500 g (1 lb) salami sausage, cut into chunks

250 g (8 oz) piece smoked bacon, cut into chunks

6 small onions

6 cloves

3¾ cups (940 ml/30 fl oz) water

2 bay leaves

1 bouquet garni

1½ kg (3 lb) small potatoes, peeled

1¼ cups (315 ml/10 fl oz) dry white wine

seasonings, to taste

Place salami and bacon in a large pan with whole onions, each studded with a clove.

Add water, bay leaves and bouquet garni. Bring to the boil. Simmer for 40 minutes. Skim off any fat.

Stir in remaining ingredients. Simmer for a further 30 minutes or until potatoes are tender. Serve with vegetables in season and crusty bread.

SERVES 4 TO 6

BLANCHING

Blanching is when a food is dropped into boiling water for 30 seconds to 1 minute to partially cook it. It is then refreshed under cold running water to stop the cooking process.

CAULIFLOWER AND TOMATO

1 cauliflower, cut into florets

500 g (1 lb) tomatoes, peeled and chopped

seasonings, to taste

125 g (4 oz) butter or margarine, melted

½ cup (60 g/2 oz) fresh breadcrumbs

½ cup (60 g/2 oz) grated tasty cheese

½ cup (60 g/2 oz) grated Parmesan cheese

Preheat oven to 190°C (375°F).

Cook the cauliflower in boiling water until tender. Drain and refresh under cold running water. Place cauliflower and tomatoes in a greased casserole dish. Sprinkle with seasonings.

Pour half the butter over the cauliflower. Sprinkle with combined breadcrumbs and cheeses. Pour over remaining butter.

Bake for 30 minutes or until golden. Serve as a meal accompaniment or with salad and crusty bread.

SERVES 4 TO 6

VEGETABLE CURRY

⅓ cup oil (80 ml/3 fl oz)

2 teaspoons cumin

½ teaspoon turmeric

¼ teaspoon chilli powder

2 onions, chopped

2 cloves garlic, crushed

small piece ginger root, grated

2 large tomatoes, peeled and chopped

4 potatoes, quartered

¼ head cauliflower, cut into florets

3 to 4 zucchini (courgettes), sliced

½ eggplant (aubergine), diced

1 cup (125 g/4 oz) frozen peas

½ cup (125 ml/4 fl oz) water

Heat oil and stir in cumin, turmeric and chilli powder. Add onions, garlic and ginger and sauté, stirring until onions are soft but not brown. Add all vegetables except the peas and sauté, stirring, for 5 minutes.

Add water, cover and simmer over low heat for 20 minutes. Add peas and simmer 5 minutes more. Most of the moisture should be absorbed during cooking. Serve with rice.

SERVES 4

CARROT AND MUSHROOM CASSEROLE

30 g (1 oz) butter or margarine

1 onion, chopped

1 kg (2 lb) carrots, sliced

1 tablespoon tomato paste

1½ cups (375 ml/12 fl oz) water

1 stock cube, crumbled

250 g (8 oz) button mushrooms

½ cup (125 ml/4 fl oz) sherry

pinch each mace and oregano

seasonings, to taste

1 tablespoon chopped fresh chives

Melt butter in a large saucepan. Sauté onion until tender. Add carrots and tomato paste. Cook for 1 minute.

Blend in water and stock cube. Bring to the boil. Simmer, uncovered, for 30 minutes.

Stir in mushrooms, sherry, spices and seasonings. Simmer for a further 10 minutes. Sprinkle with chives. Serve as a delicious meal accompaniment for roast pork or lamb.

SERVES 4 TO 6

Artichokes with Lemon

ARTICHOKES WITH LEMON

3 artichokes

1 tablespoon olive oil

500 g (1 lb) asparagus, cut into 5 cm (2 in) lengths

1 lemon, sliced

1 cup (250 ml/8 fl oz) white wine

1 cup (250 ml/8 fl oz) vegetable stock

1 teaspoon freshly ground black pepper

2 tablespoons chopped fresh, mixed herbs

Place artichokes in a large saucepan of simmering water. Simmer for 30 to 40 minutes or until soft.

Heat oil in a frying pan. Sauté asparagus and lemon for 5 minutes or until tender. Remove from pan. Set aside. Pour wine and stock into same pan. Simmer for 5 minutes or until reduced by half.

Return asparagus and lemon to pan with pepper and herbs. Slice artichokes in half. Remove choke (at base of artichoke). Add artichokes to pan with sauce. Simmer for 3 minutes or until heated through.

SERVES 6

RATATOUILLE

2 eggplants (aubergines), sliced

salt

2 red or green capsicums (peppers), seeded and halved

½ cup (125 ml/4 fl oz) olive oil

4 zucchini (courgettes), cut into strips

2 onions, chopped

3 cloves garlic, crushed

850 g (1 lb 11 oz) canned tomatoes, chopped

½ cup (125 ml/4 fl oz) red wine

2 tablespoons tomato paste

½ cup (80 g/2½ oz) black olives

2 to 3 tablespoons chopped fresh mixed herbs

seasonings, to taste

Sprinkle eggplants with salt. Leave for 30 minutes. Rinse well. Pat dry. Set aside.

Place capsicums under a hot grill, skin side up. Cook until skins blacken. Place in a plastic bag for 5 minutes. Peel and discard skin. Roughly chop capsicums. Set aside.

Heat half the oil in a large saucepan. Sauté zucchini, onions and garlic until golden. Blend in tomatoes, wine and tomato paste. Simmer for 5 minutes.

Heat remaining oil in a frying pan. Cook eggplant slices until golden each

Ratatouille

side. Stir into tomato mixture with capsicum. Simmer for 15 minutes.

Blend in olives, herbs and seasonings. Simmer for 1 minute.

SERVES 4 TO 6

EGGPLANT (AUBERGINES)

When eggplants (aubergines) are sliced and salted, this is called 'degorging'. This process draws out moisture and any bitterness.

EGGPLANT AND PASTA CASSEROLE

1 eggplant (aubergine), sliced

salt

250 g (8 oz) noodles or macaroni

2 tablespoons oil

3 tomatoes, peeled and chopped

2 onions, chopped

1 green capsicum (pepper), seeded and chopped

1 clove garlic, crushed

1 red chilli, sliced (optional)

125 g (4 oz) canned corn kernels, drained

1½ cups (185 g/6 oz) diced, cooked beef

seasonings, to taste

60 g (2 oz) butter or margarine

4 tablespoons plain (all-purpose flour)

2 cups (500 ml/16 fl oz) stock

2 egg yolks

½ cup (30 g/1 oz) fresh breadcrumbs

30 g (1 oz) butter or margarine, extra, melted

1 teaspoon chopped fresh parsley

Preheat oven to 180°C (350°F).

Sprinkle eggplant with salt. Leave for 30 minutes. Rinse well. Pat dry. Set aside.

Cook noodles in plenty of boiling water for 10 minutes or until tender. Drain. Set aside.

Heat oil in a frying pan. Fry eggplant until golden on each side. Drain on crumpled kitchen paper. Add tomatoes, onions, garlic and chilli to the same pan. Cook for 4 minutes. Stir in corn.

Arrange eggplant, beef, vegetables and noodles in layers in a greased casserole dish. Sprinkle with seasonings.

Melt butter in a small saucepan. Add flour. Cook, stirring, for 1 minute.

Remove from heat. Gradually blend in stock. Pour over lightly beaten egg yolks.

Return mixture to saucepan. Heat gently, stirring constantly, until sauce boils and thickens. Pour sauce over noodles. Bake for 25 to 30 minutes.

Sprinkle casserole with combined breadcrumbs, butter and parsley. Bake for a further 5 minutes or until golden. Serve with salad.

SERVES 4 TO 6

GOLDEN-TOPPED VEGETABLE CASSEROLE

1 eggplant (aubergine), sliced

salt

¼ cup (60 ml/2 fl oz) olive oil

2 onions, sliced

4 zucchini (courgettes), sliced

4 tomatoes, sliced

2 carrots, sliced and blanched

2 potatoes, peeled, sliced and blanched

2 cups (250 g/8 oz) canned or fresh okra, trimmed

2 teaspoons chopped fresh parsley

2 teaspoons ground oregano

¼ teaspoon nutmeg

seasonings, to taste

1 kg (2 lb) potatoes, peeled and chopped

½ cup (60 g/2 oz) grated tasty cheese

½ cup (125 ml/4 fl oz) milk

2 eggs, separated

½ teaspoon paprika

Preheat oven to 200°C (400°F).

Sprinkle eggplant with salt. Leave for 30 minutes. Rinse well. Pat dry. Set aside.

Heat oil in a frying pan. Sauté onions until tender. Remove from pan. Fry eggplant until golden on both sides. Remove from pan.

Layer eggplant, onions, zucchini, carrots, potatoes and okra in a deep casserole dish, sprinkling each layer with a little parsley, oregano, nutmeg and seasonings. Bake, covered, for 30 minutes.

Reduce oven temperature to 190°C (375°F).

Boil potatoes until tender. Mash well. Mix mashed potato, cheese, milk egg yolks and paprika until smooth and creamy. Whisk egg whites until stiff. Beat into potato mixture. Spoon evenly over casserole. Bake for 10 to 15 minutes or until topping is golden.

SERVES 4 TO 6

CELERY AND ONION CASSEROLE

¼ cup (60 ml/2 fl oz) oil

8 rashers (250 g/8 oz) rindless bacon, chopped

250 g (8 oz) pickling onions

1 head celery, sliced into 10 cm (4 in) pieces

1 tablespoon tomato paste

2 cups (500 ml/16 fl oz) chicken stock

1 bouquet garni

seasonings, to taste

Preheat oven to 180°C (350°F).

Heat oil in a frying pan. Sauté bacon for 3 minutes. Remove from pan. Add whole onions to pan with celery. Cook for 5 minutes. Stir in tomato paste.

Blend in stock. Add bouquet garni, seasonings and bacon. Transfer mixture to a casserole dish. Bake, covered, for 35 minutes.

SERVES 4 TO 6

LENTIL BEAN STEW

1 cup (200 g/6½ oz) butter beans

1 cup (220 g/7 oz) chickpeas

vegetable stock

1 cup (200 g/6½ oz) lentils

1 green capsicum (pepper), roughly chopped

1 red capsicum (pepper), roughly chopped

4 sticks celery, thickly sliced

2 carrots, chopped

250 g (8 oz) tomatoes, peeled

310 g (10 oz) canned corn kernels

2 tablespoons tomato paste

bouquet garni

salt and freshly ground black pepper

Soak beans and chick peas overnight in water to cover. Drain and measure liquid, adding stock to make up to 600 ml (2½ cups/1 pt).

Place all ingredients in a saucepan and bring to the boil very slowly — it should take about 30 minutes — then simmer for 1–1½ hours or until beans and chick peas are tender. Remove bouquet garni and season to taste.

SERVES 6

BARLEY VEGETABLE CASSEROLE

⅔ cup (125 g/4 oz) pearl barley

2½ cups (600 ml/1 pt) vegetable stock

1 tablespoon oil

1 clove garlic, crushed

1 onion, chopped

2 sticks celery, chopped

2 carrots, finely diced

2 tablespoons tomato paste

1 cup (125 g/4 oz) frozen peas

Soak barley overnight in stock. Bring to the boil and simmer for 1 hour. Drain barley and reserve liquid.

Heat oil and sauté garlic, onion, celery and carrots for 8 minutes, stirring occasionally to prevent them from browning. Add tomato paste and cook for 1 minute, then add barley, stock and peas. Simmer for 20 minutes, until vegetables are tender and liquid has almost evaporated. Add barley and reheat.

SERVES 4

BOSTON BAKED BEANS

500 g (1 lb) haricot beans, soaked in water overnight

7 cups (1¾ litres/50 fl oz) water

4 rashers (125 g/4 oz) rindless bacon (optional), cubed

1 onion, finely chopped

2 tablespoons black treacle

1 tablespoon tomato paste

1 tablespoon mustard powder

1 tablespoon Worcestershire sauce

1 tablespoon vinegar

pinch ground cloves

seasonings, to taste

Preheat oven to 150°C (300°F).

Drain the haricot beans. Place them in a large saucepan with water. Bring to the boil. Reduce heat. Simmer for 45 minutes, removing any scum that rises to the surface.

Transfer the beans and liquid to a large casserole dish. Stir in remaining ingredients. Bake, covered, for 2 hours. Remove lid. Bake for another 30 minutes or until beans are tender.

SERVES 6 TO 8

WILD RICE AND MUSHROOM CASSEROLE

Wild rice is nutritious. It is however rather expensive so if you want to make larger quantities, use a combination of ordinary rice.

⅔ cup wild rice

3 cups (750 ml/1 pt 4 fl oz) boiling water

40 g (2½ oz) butter

½ onion, finely chopped

60 g/2 oz mushrooms, finely chopped

1 tablespoon plain (all-purpose) flour

1 cup (250 ml/8 fl oz) vegetable stock

salt and freshly ground black pepper

2 tablespoons blanched slivered almonds

Wash rice and soak overnight in cold water. Wash and change cold water serveral times.

Preheat oven to 180°C (350°F).

Stir rice into boiling water. Cover and boil 5 minutes, drain and wash again. Add rice and salt to 3 cups (750 ml/1 pt 4 fl oz) boiling water, cover and cook until tender, about 20 minutes.

Melt butter in a saucepan and sauté onions and mushrooms in butter for 5 minutes. Blend in flour with a wooden spoon and gradually add stock, stirring constantly, until smooth and thick. Season to taste and mix with cooked rice. Turn into buttered shallow casserole and, sprinkle with almonds and bake for 20 minutes.

SERVES 4

CARROT CASSEROLE

2½ cups (315 g/10 oz) sliced carrots

1 onion, finely chopped

½ cup (125 ml/4 fl oz) water

seasonings, to taste

¼ cup (30 g/1 oz) soy grits

¼ cup (30 g/1 oz) sunflower seeds

2 tablespoons snipped dill

1 tablespoon honey

1 egg, lightly beaten

½ cup (60 g/2 oz) chopped almonds

Preheat oven to 180°C (350°F).

Place carrots, onion, water and seasonings into a saucepan. Bring to the boil. Simmer, covered, for 3 minutes or until carrots are tender.

Stir all remaining ingredients, except almonds, into carrot mixture. Pour mixture into a shallow casserole dish. Sprinkle with almonds. Bake for 15 minutes.

SERVES 4 TO 6

ARABIAN MIXED VEGETABLES

2 tablespoons oil

1 onion, finely chopped

1 bay leaf

Carrot Casserole

¾ teaspoon mustard seeds

½ teaspoon dried dill

¼ teaspoon celery seeds

500 g (1 lb) cauliflower, cut into florets

2 tomatoes, peeled and chopped

2 zucchini (courgettes), sliced

1 potato, peeled and chopped

1 carrot, sliced

1 green apple, cored and chopped

½ teaspoon paprika

Heat oil in a large, heavy-based pan. Sauté onion, bay leaf, mustard seeds, dill and celery seeds until onion is tender but not brown.

Arabian Mixed Vegetables

Add cauliflower, tomatoes, zucchini, potato, carrot and apple. Sauté for 3 minutes. Cook, stirring, for 20 minutes or until vegetables are tender. Serve sprinkled with paprika.

SERVES 4 TO 6

CAPSICUM WITH PINE NUT FILLING

6 large green capsicum (peppers)

⅓ cup (60 g/2 oz) long grain rice

3 tablespoons olive oil

1 onion, chopped

2 tablespoons pine nuts

2 cloves garlic, crushed

500 g (1 lb) chicken or lamb mince

1½ cups (375 ml/12 oz) tomato juice

¼ cup (30 g/1 oz) raisins

2 tablespoons honey

¼ teaspoon thyme

pinch ground ginger

seasonings, to taste

Preheat oven to 190°C (375°F).

Cut a slice from the top of each capsicum. If they don't stand upright, cut a thin slice from the base. Remove all seeds and membrane. Blanch in boiling water for 2 minutes. Drain thoroughly.

Cook rice in boiling water until just tender. Drain thoroughly.

Heat half the oil in a frying pan. Sauté onion, pine nuts and garlic until onion is tender. Add mince. Cook, stirring for 5 minutes or until browned.

Mix in rice, ⅔ cup (155 ml/5 fl oz) tomato juice, raisins, honey, thyme, ginger and seasonings.

Brush outside of capsicum with oil. Fill with mince mixture. Arrange in a shallow casserole dish.

Pour tomato juice and any remaining oil over and around capsicums. Bake for 45 minutes, basting occasionally. Serve with sauce.

SERVES 6

Capsicum with Pine Nut Filling Cut slice from top of each capsicum. Remove seeds and membrane.

Cook filling ingredients over low heat.

Stuff capsicum with filling mixture. Arrange in shallow casserole and pour over remaining tomato juice and oil.

OKRA, CORN AND TOMATO HOTPOT

4 rashers (125 g/4 oz) rindless
    bacon, sliced

200 g (8 oz) fresh or canned
    okra, cut into 5 mm (¼ in slices

1 onion, finely chopped

315 g (10 oz) canned corn
    kernels, drained

3 tomatoes, peeled and chopped

1 green capsicum (pepper),
    seeded and chopped

few drops Tabasco sauce

seasonings, to taste

Fry bacon until crisp. Drain on
crumpled kitchen paper. When cool,
crumble. Set aside.

Sauté okra and onion in bacon oil
until onion is tender. Stir in corn.
Cook, stirring, for 3 minutes.

Stir in all remaining ingredients.
Simmer, covered, for 20 minutes or
until vegetables are tender. Serve as
a meal accompaniment, sprinkled
with bacon.

SERVES 4 TO 6

LAYERED VEGETABLE MORNAY

1 tablespoon oil

1 onion, finely chopped

250 g (8 oz) button mushrooms,
    sliced

½ red capsicum (pepper), seeded
    and chopped

½ green capsicum (pepper),
    seeded and chopped

425 g (13½ oz) canned tomatoes,
    drained and chopped

¼ cup (60 g/2 oz) tomato paste

2 tablespoons chopped fresh basil

1 teaspoon sugar

6 zucchini (courgettes), trimmed
    and sliced into sticks

grated Parmesan cheese

SPINACH LAYER

1 bunch English spinach or
    silverbeet (Swiss chard),
    washed, stalks removed and
    chopped

1 onion, finely chopped

1 clove garlic, crushed

¼ teaspoon nutmeg

MORNAY LAYER

¾ cup (185 ml/6 fl oz) milk

1 onion, chopped

4 cloves

1 bay leaf

30 g (1 oz) butter or margarine

2 tablespoons plain (all-purpose)
    flour

½ cup (60 g/2 oz) grated tasty
    cheese

CHEESE LAYER

500 g (1 lb) ricotta cheese

½ cup (60 g/2 oz) grated
    Parmesan cheese

2 eggs, beaten

Preheat oven to 180°C (350°F).

Heat the oil in a large frying pan.
Sauté onion until tender. Add
mushrooms and capsicum. Sauté
until tender.

Stir in the tomatoes, tomato paste,
basil and sugar. Simmer, uncovered,
for 30 minutes. Set aside.

To Prepare Spinach Layer: Place all
ingredients in a large saucepan.
Cook, covered, for 3 to 5 minutes
or until leaves wilt. Drain well,
squeezing spinach to remove all
excess water.

To Prepare Mornay Layer: Heat milk
with onion, cloves and bay leaf until
almost boiling. Strain, discarding
flavourings. Set aside.

Melt butter in a saucepan. Add flour.
Cook, stirring, for 1 minute.
Remove from heat. Gradually blend
in milk. Return to heat. Cook,
stirring constantly, until sauce boils
and thickens. Blend in cheese.

Cover surface with plastic wrap
until required.

To Prepare Cheese Layer: Combine
all ingredients. Set aside.

Pour half the vegetable mixture into
a greased casserole dish. Top with a
layer of zucchini. Spread spinach
mixture over this, followed by the
remaining vegetable mixture and
cheese mixture.

Cover with remaining zucchini strips.
Pour over mornay sauce. Sprinkle
with Parmesan cheese. Bake for 40
to 45 minutes or until golden and
bubbling. Serve with crusty bread
and salad.

SERVES 4 TO 6

COOKED SPINACH

Remove excess water from cooked spinach
by pressing it firmly between two plates or
pushing it firmly into fine sieve.

NOODLES WITH BEANS AND TOMATO

850 g (1 lb 11 oz) canned
    tomatoes, chopped

250 g (8 oz) green beans,
    trimmed and sliced

4 cups (1 litre/32 fl oz) water

70 g (2½ oz) egg noodles

1 onion, chopped

2 tablespoons olive oil

1 clove garlic, crushed

1 teaspoon chopped basil

seasonings, to taste

½ cup (60 g/2 oz) grated tasty
    cheese

1 tomato, chopped

Place the tomatoes and beans in a
large saucepan with water. Bring to

the boil. Simmer for 15 minutes. Add noodles. Cook until tender.

Process onion, oil, garlic, basil and seasonings in a food processor or blender until smooth and creamy.

Whisk into tomato mixture. Heat gently. Top with cheese and tomato. Serve with crusty bread.

SERVES 4 TO 6

BEANS, TOMATO AND HERBS

⅓ cup (90 ml/3 fl oz) olive oil

2 onions, finely chopped

3 cloves garlic, crushed

6 tomatoes, peeled

water

bouquet garni

seasonings, to taste

1 kg (2 lb) green beans, trimmed

2 tablespoons chopped fresh parsley

Heat oil in a large pan. Sauté onions and garlic until onions are tender.

Squeeze tomatoes into a sieve to remove seeds. Reserve juice. Discard seeds. Make up to ⅔ cup (155 ml/ 5 fl oz) liquid with water. Chop the tomato flesh.

Add tomatoes, tomato liquid, bouquet garni and seasonings to onions and garlic. Bring to the boil. Reduce heat. Simmer for 30 minutes.

Add beans to pan. Simmer for 5 to 10 minutes or until tender. Serve sprinkled with parsley.

SERVES 4 TO 6

TOMATOES

The term 'concasse' means to peel, seed and chop tomatoes.

Vegetable Makeover

*T*o modify this recipe to a healthier version, reducing fat, kilojoules and cholesterol:

Skin is left on potatoes, increasing fibre and retaining nutrients.

Ham is used in place of bacon.

Butter has been reduced by 75 per cent and has been replaced with polyunsaturated margarine.

Low fat or low cholesterol cheese has been used in place of full fat cheese.

No salt has been used.

Extra herbs have been added to improve flavour.

HAM, CHEESE AND POTATO BAKE

1kg (2 lb) potatoes, scrubbed and thinly sliced

1 clove garlic, crushed

125 g (4 oz) ham, chopped

1 cup (125 g/4 oz) grated low fat or low cholesterol cheese

½ teaspoon ground nutmeg

freshly ground black pepper, to taste

2½ cups (625 ml/21 fl oz) chicken stock

30 g (1 oz) polyunsaturated margarine

1 tablespoon chopped fresh mixed herbs

Preheat oven to 180°C (350°F).

Place a layer of potatoes on the base of a lightly greased casserole dish. Sprinkle with garlic. Continue layering with ham, half the cheese and remaining potato, sprinkling with nutmeg and pepper between each layer. Finish with a potato layer.

Pour over stock. Bake for 30 minutes. Remove from oven. Sprinkle with remaining cheese. Dot with margarine. Bake for a further 20 minutes or until golden. Serve sprinkled with herbs.

SERVES 4 TO 6

VEGETABLE HOTPOT WITH CAPERS

3 tablespoons oil

1 onion, chopped

1 clove garlic, crushed

1 cauliflower, cut into florets

6 tomatoes, peeled and chopped

1 green capsicum (pepper), seeded and chopped

seasonings, to taste

1 tablespoon chopped fresh parsley

1 teaspoon chopped capers

Heat oil in a large saucepan. Sauté onion and garlic until onion is tender. Add cauliflower. Cook, covered, over a gentle heat for 10 minutes. Stir occasionally.

Stir in tomatoes, capsicum and seasonings. Simmer for 5 minutes. Serve, sprinkled with combined parsley and capers.

SERVES 4 TO 6

HARD-BOILED EGGS

Cook hard-boiled eggs by placing eggs (at room temperature) into gently simmering water (if from the refrigerator, place into cold water and bring to the boil). Cook for 6 minutes. Place under cold running water to cool. Remove shells. Use as directed.

Vegetable Hotpot with Capers

SPANISH EGG CASSEROLE

125 g (4 oz) butter or margarine

2 sticks celery, chopped

1 onion, chopped

1 red or green capsicum (pepper), seeded and chopped

2 tablespoons plain (all-purpose) flour

850 g (1 lb 11 oz) canned tomatoes, chopped

¼ teaspoon cayenne pepper

seasonings, to taste

12 hard-boiled eggs, chopped

360 g (11½ oz) canned champignons, drained and chopped

1 cup (250 ml/8 fl oz) white sauce (see recipe p XX)

½ cup (30 g/1 oz) fresh breadcrumbs

½ cup (60 g/2 oz) grated tasty cheese

finely chopped fresh parsley

Preheat oven to 220°C (425°F).

Melt half of the butter in a large frying pan. Sauté celery, onion and capsicum until onion is tender.

Stir in flour. Cook 1 minute. Blend in tomatoes with juice and seasonings. Bring to the boil, stirring constantly.

Mix in the eggs, champignons and sauce. Spoon mixture into individual serving dishes or a casserole dish. Top with combined breadcrumbs and cheese. Dot remaining with butter.

Bake for 10 minutes or until golden and bubbling. Sprinkle with parsley. Serve with crusty bread.

SERVES 4 TO 6

Add tomatoes and flour to fried onion, capsicum and celery.

Pour in the tomato juice and seasonings.

Stir in the white sauce.

Stir in the chopped eggs and champignons.

BRAISED ZUCCHINI AND TOMATO

90 g (3 oz) butter or margarine

750 g (1½ lb) zucchini (courgettes), trimmed and sliced into sticks

3 tomatoes, peeled and chopped

¼ cup (60 ml/2 fl oz) dry white wine

seasonings, to taste

1 tablespoon chopped fresh dill

Melt butter in a large frying pan. Sauté zucchini for 3 to 4 minutes.

Stir in tomatoes, wine and seasonings. Simmer, covered, for 5 minutes. Serve with grilled or barbecued meat, sprinkled with dill.

SERVES 4 TO 6

Braised Zucchini and Tomato

OVEN TEMPERATURES

TEMPERATURES	CELSIUS (°C)	FAHRENHEIT (°F)	GAS MARK
Very slow	120	250	½
Slow	150	300	2
Moderately slow	160-180	325-350	3-4
Moderate	190-200	375-400	5-6
Moderately hot	220-230	425-450	7
Hot	250-260	475-500	8-9

NOTE: We developed the recipes in this book in Australia where the tablespoon measure is 20 ml. In many other countries the tablespoon is 15 ml. For most recipes this difference will not be noticeable.

However, for recipes using baking powder, gelatine, bicarbonate of soda, small amounts of flour and cornflour, we suggest you add an extra teaspoon for each tablespoon specified.

GLOSSARY OF TERMS

AUSTRALIAN	UK	USA
beetroot	beetroot	beet
black olive	black olive	ripe olive
blade steak	shoulder or chuck steak	blade/chuck steak
broad bean	broad bean	fava bean
butternut pumpkin		butternut squash
calamari	squid	calamari
capsicum	pepper	sweet pepper
chicken breasts fillets	chicken breast fillets	boneless chicken breasts
chickpea	chickpea	garbanzo bean
chilli	chilli	chili
chump chop (lamb)	chump chop	leg chop
coriander (fresh)	coriander/Indian parsley	cilantro/Chinese parsley
cornflour	cornflour	cornstarch
cornmeal	polenta/maize meal	cornmeal
cream	single cream	light cream
dill	dill	dill weed
eggplant	aubergine	eggplant
fish cutlet	fish cutlet	fish steak
frying pan	frying pan	skillet
gammon/ham steak	gammon	ham/picnic shoulder
grill	grill	broil
minced beef	minced beef	ground beef
paper towel	absorbent kitchen paper	paper towel
pine nut	pine nut	pignolias
plain flour	(general purpose) flour	all-purpose flour
pork fillet	pork fillet	pork tenderloin
rasher (bacon)	rasher	slice
rump steak	rump steak	sirloin
shallots	spring onions	scallions/green onions
shin (of beef)		shank
silver beet (spinach)	silver beet (chard)	Swiss chard
stock cube	stock cube	bouillon cube
tomato paste	tomato purée	tomato paste
tomato purée	tomato purée	tomato paste
topside beef	topside beef	round beef
topside steak		round steak
zucchini	courgette	zucchini

INDEX